# Never Such Innocence
# The Centenary of
# the First World War

# Never Such Innocence
# The Centenary of
# the First World War

*Children's Responses through Poetry, Art and Song*

Frontispiece: Detail of WW1 Quilt *by Henry VIII and Cantref Primary, Abergavenny;
Osbaston CW School, Monmouth; Usk CW School and Caldicot Primary*
– special commendation 2017/18.

# CONTENTS

Foreword                          6
Introduction:
Never Such Innocence              7
Map of Contributors               12

**2014**                          **14**
Introduction                      16
Ages 9–11                         18
Ages 11–14                        22
Ages 14–16                        32

**2015/16**                       **42**
Introduction                      44
Ages 9–11                         46
Ages 11–14                        58
Ages 14–16                        68
Gaelic Winner                     78
Royal Navy Battle of Jutland
Commemorations                    79
Our Youngest Contributors         82

**2016/17**                       **84**
Introduction                      86
Ages 9–11                         88
Ages 11–14                        100
Ages 14–16                        110
Gaelic Winner                     124
Welsh Winner                      125

**2017/18**                       **126**
Introduction                      128

Ages 9–11                         130
Ages 11–14                        140
Ages 14–16                        152
Gaelic Winner                     162
Welsh Winner                      164
Special Commendation              166

**The Royal British Legion –**
**Thank You**                     **170**
Ages 9–11                         170
Ages 11– 14                       172
Ages 14–16                        175
Song: Ages 9–11                   179

**War in the Skies**             **180**
Ages 9–11                         180
Ages 11–14                        186
Ages 14–16                        190

**Songs of the Centenary**       **194**

**Together: A UK–German**
**Centenary Project**            **200**
Introduction                      202
Ages 9–11                         204
Ages 11–14                        206
Ages 14–16                        208
Song: Ages 11–14                  210

Acknowledgements                  216

Never Such Innocence has played a unique and vitally important part in marking the centenary of the First World War. It has dovetailed closely with the wider series of 2014–18 centenary events coordinated by Her Majesty's Government. I had been following NSI's progress with much interest, not least in my role as Vice Chairman of the Commonwealth War Graves Commission, and I was delighted and honoured to become the charity's President in November 2016, in succession to the late 6th Duke of Westminster, who played such a crucial role in its early years.

From the beginning, Never Such Innocence has had a very simple objective: to engage children and young people from around the world in the centenary through poetry, art and song. We have introduced these 'custodians of the future' to the facts about the Great War, then given them an opportunity to have a say on what war means to them – to give their 21st century perspective on the events of 1914–18.

This charming book will give you an insight into how they have responded to that challenge. I have been consistently impressed with the calibre of entries received, and fascinated by how quickly they have picked up the emotions and currents which ran through the Great War. It is instructive to listen to these young voices; to ponder on the different perspectives that these fresh young eyes and ears bring to that terrible war which has shaped so much of the world around us.

I would like to pay a warm tribute to everyone who has taken part: teachers, families and, most importantly, the thousands of young people from around the world. You have created a powerful legacy, and I am delighted that it will be shared with a wider public.

*Tim Laurence*

Vice Admiral Sir Tim Laurence
KCVO, CB, ADC(P)

## NEVER SUCH INNOCENCE – A SMALL IDEA THAT GREW AND GREW

In order to relate the story of Never Such Innocence (NSI), I must first give you a little of my background. I grew up the last of four daughters, and from the nursery I was told stories of my great-grandfather Field Marshal Sir John French and his life during both the Boer War and the First World War. I think the motivation behind these stories was twofold: firstly, to instil in me my family's history, and secondly and perhaps more truthfully, I am convinced my father wanted me to be a boy!

Whatever the reason, 'The Old Boy', as he was endearingly called at home, was very much part of my upbringing. When I heard the then Prime Minister David Cameron in winter 2012 talk about the forthcoming Centenary of the First World War in 2014, I felt compelled to 'do' something… the question was: what?

The answer didn't take long at all: it would be far too easy to leave the Centenary to historians, academics and, well, grown-ups! I wanted to give children and young people a strong and powerful voice during those all-important Centenary years. And so the Poetry, Art and Song (in 2016-17) Competition began its journey! Dr Martin Stephen, one of our trustees, had previously published an anthology of First World War poetry and had aptly entitled it Never Such Innocence, a line from 'MCMXIV', a poem by Philip Larkin. What could be a better name for a First World War Centenary charity established to engage children in the events of 100 years ago? Martin kindly agreed that we use his title. The charity had a name!

I must mention our marvellous founding President, the late Gerald Grosvenor, 6th Duke of Westminster, who sadly died in summer 2016, and offer my profuse and heartfelt thanks to his successor, Vice Admiral Sir Tim Laurence, who so ably took the helm and has navigated us brilliantly through the intervening years.

How were we to engage with children and young people? We needed a resource: a high-quality, child-friendly book to tell the story of this monumental period of our shared history. I am certainly no historian, and we needed a bright, dynamic, wordsmith who could research and write and lure historians to our aid. We were blessed to meet and subsequently employ Lucy Kentish. Lucy lovingly compiled the resource that we send, free of charge, to schools around the world – this book is now available for sale as *Stories of the First World War*. Five years on, Lucy remains the NSI guardian angel! Our team has grown, and both Maddie Messenger and Eleanor Stephens have proved invaluable sources of youth, energy and ideas!

We launched the project in May 2014 at the splendid Australian High Commission. Martin wrote a script, a journey through the Great War in poetry and song, to be performed by some marvellous actors, including Tim McInnerny, Mark Field, Polly Hemingway and Charlotte Newton John. The evenings – we did two – were narrated by the illustrious and much-loved John Julius Norwich who so very sadly died this summer (2018). All in all, we set the scene for our ambitions, but were still unsure of quite how far and wide we could take the project. We thought we would reach out to schools in England: we did, in a very small, tentative way, and received in the first year 500 entries… We were stunned, delighted and spurred on to be more ambitious!

We were fearful of being London-centric, as a Londoner born and bred, I was keen that we cut the umbilical cord of the capital and visit the length and breadth of the United Kingdom. We embarked on a series of annual Roadshows. We visited communities far and wide, from Blackwood to Belfast, Shetland to Sunderland, Germany to Greece, Yorkshire to Hampshire. We travelled by car, rail and aeroplane; we contended with hurricanes, fog and sleeper trains! Our NSI children have stood in chilly aircraft hangars ogling Chinooks and Typhoons, clambered aboard warships, and seen some of the most splendid buildings the UK and

Europe have to offer. The whole idea has been to get children out of school (where necessary we cover all costs), and then to experience something unique, exciting and memorable, in doing so breaking down barriers and enabling them to believe that anything is possible.

The NSI team have loved every minute of this journey of discovery, meeting extraordinary children and communities whilst forging long-lasting friendships.

At each roadshow, children take to the stage and recite or sing work they have produced, showcasing their creativity and thought. We also bring with us one of our brilliant partners, the Commonwealth War Graves Commission, who tell those assembled about the important work of the commission and, importantly, where local CWGC graves are. We assemble as the audience the 'good and the great' of the community – the Lord Lieutenant, the Lord Mayor, the local MP and representatives of the Armed Forces – and make clear from the outset that the children are our VVIPS. That

the good and the great are here to listen to their voices. We want to hear what the custodians of the future have to say about the events of 100 years ago, events that changed their world.

From the outset, one of our fundamental objectives has been to ensure that we empower these custodians of the future. We do this in a number of ways: through our roadshows; and by giving a personalised certificate to each and every entrant, thereby highlighting that every child and young person participating has done something important for the Centenary. It is delightfully reassuring that in the technological 21st century children still feel excited about a certificate! We also ensure that our children are included in the official First World War national commemorations. Children have played their part in the commemorations of the Battle of Jutland and the Battle of Passchendaele. (See pages 44–45 for more about these special days.)

For 2018 we launched a brand-new strand of the project and entitled it

Together. We encouraged German and UK children to work 'together' to create messages of hope and unity for the future. The results have been inspiring and life-affirming. (A selection of Together entries can be found on pages 200–215.)

We recognise the winners of each Competition at an annual Awards Ceremony. We started off small, at a law firm in the City, but as our ambitions grew for more entries so did our choice of venues! Year two was held at the House of Lords, and the 2016/17 Awards and final Centenary Awards were held in the splendid confines of the Guards' Chapel at Wellington Barracks, by kind permission of Major General Ben Bathurst.

For our final Awards we decided to pull out all the stops! We had the Band of the Scots Guards, the Drum Corps of Her Majesty's Royal Marines, the RAF Queen's Colour Squadron and a helicopter! We were welcomed by the Reverend Stephen Dunwoody, the Awards were introduced by our President, Vice Admiral Sir Tim Laurence, and our prize-giver was the Vice Chief of the Defence Staff, General Sir Gordon Messenger. Other notable guests included the Vice Chief of the Air Staff, Air Vice Marshal Mike Wigston; Islamic Advisor to the Ministry of Defence, Imam Asim Hafiz; Her Majesty's Lord-Lieutenant for Greater London, Sir Ken Olisa; and a brilliant selection of cross-party MPs. We received special messages from the Prime Minister, the Rt Hon Theresa May MP; the Secretary of State for Digital, Culture, Media and Sport, the Rt Hon Matt Hancock MP; and the Secretary of State for Defence, the Rt Hon Gavin Williamson MP. It was quite a day!

I have consistently found the children's work poignant, thoughtful and thought-provoking, as have our judges, who have deliberated hard to make the selections each and every year: our final Centenary year was perhaps the most taxing, having received 7,136 brilliant entries!

Children have travelled to our Awards from every corner of the United

Kingdom and, to our delight, from across the world. For 2017/18, children travelled from Sunderland, Lossiemouth, Sheffield, Anglesey and Belfast, to name but a few places in the UK, and from Canada, the USA, Malaysia, Romania, Greece and France more globally.

We have now had young people from 47 countries, territories and dependencies participate… spanning five continents! This extraordinarily international response to the events of 100 years ago has been phenomenal.

Our Centenary finale at Buckingham Palace in 2018 saw children from the four years come together. Our eldest 2014 winners, now aged 20, mingling with our 2017/18 winners, some as young as nine. All have created a body of work that I hope will move you, make you ponder and reflect on the Centenary and the inspirational descendants the First World War has given us.

Over the NSI years I have alluded to acorns and oak trees to emphasise the might and scale of what our NSI young people have achieved. For this anthology, imagine a forest filled with trees from every continent standing tall, remembering the sacrifices made 100 years ago. Everyone who has contributed to NSI over these four years has built this forest, and I thank them for it.

I hope you enjoy these creative reflections… a Children's Centenary Legacy.

Lady Lucy French

## MAP OF CONTRIBUTORS

**Never Such Innocence received poetry, art and songs from children from the following 47 countries, territories and dependencies:**

Australia
Belgium
Bulgaria
Canada
China
England
Former Yugoslav Republic
of Macedonia
France
Germany
Gibraltar
Greece
Guernsey
India
Indonesia
Isle of Man
Italy
Japan
Jersey
Kingdom of Bahrain
Lithuania
Malaysia
Malta
New Zealand
Nigeria
Northern Ireland
Philippines
Poland
Portugal
Puerto Rico
Republic of Ireland
Romania
Rwanda

Saudi Arabia
Scotland
Serbia
Singapore
South Africa
South Korea
Sri Lanka
Switzerland
Thailand
The Netherlands
Turkey
Ukraine
United Arab Emirates
USA
Wales

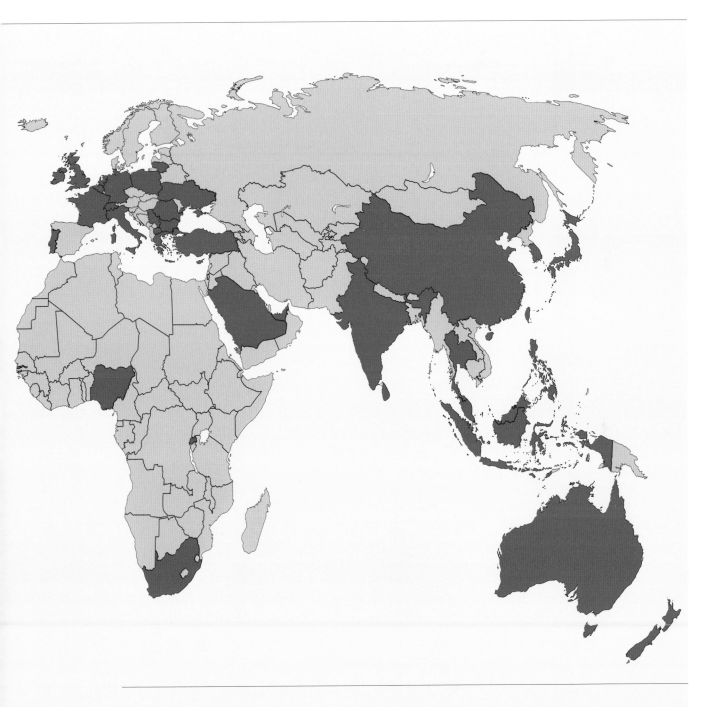

2014

Never Such Innocence launched its Poetry and Art Competition in 2014; it was aimed at young people aged 11 to 16. Entrants were encouraged to choose a topic related to the First World War and produce a piece of art or write a poem inspired by what they had learned. A creative response to the events of 100 years ago. To inspire entries, we produced a 56-page resource, a child-friendly journey through the First World War that included contributions from historians, academics, our friends and partners. We created characters Nurse Elsie and Sergeant Bert to accompany readers as they learned about the War.

The Competition was launched in September 2014 at Marylebone Boys' School with the then Lord Mayor of Westminster, Councillor Audrey Lewis; the then Mayor of Brent, Councillor Kana Naheerathan; the former Ambassador of Ireland to Great Britain, HE Daniel Mulhall; and the MP for the Cities of London and Westminster, Rt Hon Mark Field. We received an enthusiastic response from schools, and to our surprise and delight we received poetry submissions from primary schools. In response to this interest, we swiftly created a separate category in order to recognise the work of children aged 9 to 11.

During the 2014 Competition our resource was directly received by 538 schools and downloaded more than 1,000 times. We received 183 entries for the art competition and 376 entries for the poetry competition. Following the success of the pilot, we developed the competition by introducing a permanent category for 9-to-11-year-olds, and committed ourselves to updating the resource annually to introduce additional personal stories, country profiles and battlefronts.

The 2014 Never Such Innocence Competition was supported by the Westminster Foundation, CH2M and the Macintosh Foundation.

**AGES 9–11**

## The Love of a Mother
*by Melissa Kastrati from Eglinton Primary School, London*

I miss my son.
He was the sun on my face.
But then he left without a trace.
He fights in the war,
He fights for peace.

I lay here,
I cry every night,
Who will stop the fight,
My son's in danger,
I can't say he's safe and hug him,
My faith has faded, over the last 3 anxious years
But he is still in my heart,
I pray every morning,
I pray that he's safe.

I hope he'll come back,
I hope he's thinking about me,
Don't forget me, son,
Stay strong for me
Come back home soon,
I believe in you,
You'll come back strong,
I can't live without you.

## Death

*by Victoria Gedgaudaite from Plumcroft Primary School, London*

Marching slowly towards their distant rest,
Knowing that they all did their best,
Limping, trudging, lamely like drunks,
Cursing, coughing, stumbling asleep,
Drunk with fatigue,
Death.

Memories of tragedies invade their minds,
Remembering the ones they left behind,
Thanking the gods they're still alive,
Huffing, puffing, plodding along,
Memorising the experience;
Haunting flares and guns,
Death.

Singing to lift their spirits,
Until five-nines go off,
Quick boys! Gas masks on,
Screaming in agony, crying in pain,
As memories slowly fade away,
Families will be discontented when they receive the call,
Death.

## AGES 9–11

### The Ruined Souls

*by Lydia Fisher from Plumcroft Primary School, London*

The rotting skeleton of the deserted,
ruined buildings lie on a desolate patch of rubble.
Inside is a horror, a tragic horror.
Dead bodies stacked up like books on shelves.
Flesh-eating rats flourishing off their rapidly fading souls.
Flies buzzing constantly around the bodies,
settling on wounds and infecting them.
Maggots wriggle their way into the gruesome wounds,
covering themselves in blood.
I can hear them, the deathly screams,
echoing through my mind,
as the shell screams towards them,
stealing their lives.
I can see a few stray dogs and foxes wandering the streets.
No one knows how they survived the shelling.

*'Our history is part of what makes us as a country and it is important we remember that history. Never Such Innocence is doing important work so that young people remember the sacrifice that was made so that they could have a future, and to reflect on what this means for our world today.'*

Rt Hon Theresa May MP, Prime Minister of the United Kingdom

## AGES 11–14

### Gassed

*by Amirzan Jeyakumar from Hampton School, Hampton*

AGES 11–14

## The Body of War
*by Max Park from Alleyn's School, London*

Veins of trenches down the arm,
We trudge through barren lands.
The shrieking, piercing, harsh alarm,
Shot from innocent hands.

Boys turned old in little years,
Together die in vain.
Broken eyes and shattered ears,
The unforgettable pain.

The quiet country does not know,
The soldiers story unspoken.
We now live the hell below,
The peaceful minds forever broken.

AGES 11–14

## The Women's Land Army

*by Rebekah Heath from Hope Valley College, Hope Valley*

**AGES 11–14**

## Battlefield

*by Jude Wedgwood from Hope Valley College, Hope Valley*

## AGES 11–14

**Empty Footsteps**
*by Tomas Ross-Wheeler from The Westwood Academy, Coventry*

The footprints grow as if they were there forever.
No sign of the course of these steps, just death.
The footsteps sorrow shows the longing for the owner,
But no one speaks the only words we hear are our brothers,

Brothers lost in war,
Brothers lost to the German guns,
Death calls out to us as our footstep trail ends.

**War Artist**
*by Aidan Durkin from Marylebone Boys' School, London*

Mixing

Burnt Umber
Sap Green
Payne's Grey

Cadmium Red

Dragging
Bristles
Across
The raised

Tooth

of the
Cotton duck

Observing

Recording

My Mission
My Masterpiece.

AGES 11–14

## The Man With a Sword

*by Roop Singh from Brighton College, Brighton*

AGES 11–14

## The bloody gas attack

*by Nolian Agimi from Marylebone Boys' School, London*

## AGES 11–14

### Shellshock

*by Jonathan James Kajoba from Woodbridge School, Woodbridge*

Fighting for King and Country; I volunteered to go
And now I'm at the Front line; facing the Evil Foe.
The Glory Days of Victory; are soon to be our own.
God will help the weary! Send the message home!

With every step in battle; I'm close enough to see
The enemy around us; is human, just like me.
"Hey George!" cried my mate Jonny, before the sun went down.
I saw him last in No Man's Land, but no remains were found.

They carted me to hospital; with no voice to explain
The horror of that moment; the shock; the fear; the pain.
"Chin up old son!" they said to me
"Grow up and be a man. You've lived to fight another day!"

The captain of the Regiment, sends personal regards:
"We're sorry, Mother, for your loss,
It's written in the stars, your son died for his country,
The brave and noble George; he's now with God, our Lord."

So proud am I of my dear son; who bravely fought our cause
To save our noble country, From the Kaiser's snapping jaws.
I hope he is in heaven, And not beneath the earth
Lonely in a foreign field, Far from his place of birth.

Back in Army Quarters, two officers debate
about young private George, who met with his just fate.
"Damn coward!" Charles exploded. "He tried to run away!"
"But Good old Edward caught him." They shot him at midday.

So many un-named soldiers; So many unmarked graves.
Betrayed by their own country. Tied up and whipped like slaves.
Their only guilt was trauma, their short lives full of fear.

Now George is vindicated; the lies have been exposed.
His name is clear, the stain removed; His family is told.
A letter of apology; is all they have to hold.

## AGES 14–16

## Untitled
*by Toby Mills from Alleyn's School, London*

### Frontline, Touchline – In Memory of Geoffrey Marriott
*by Sam Kaplin from University College School, London*

Leather on willow,
Followed by the ripple of gentle applause.
Bullets and mortar
Pierced the sky with a terrible roar.

I think of you,
Geoffrey Marriott, Old Gower
When I wear my UCS blazer,
Pinned with a poppy flower.

You swapped your form and deme
For name and rank
Bat and ball,
For gun and tank.

As I stumble into the examination hall with trepidation,
You marched on the battlefield with determination.
My mouth dry, in need of refreshment
Your heart pounded as heavy as the bombardment.

The schoolboy on the touchline,
The soldier on the frontline.
As I cower away from a rugby brawl
You stood under fire, proud and tall.
Killed in action, yesteryear,
So we could live today,
Without fear.

## AGES 14–16

### Forgive and Remember

*by Lydia Calman-Grimsdale from Alleyn's School, London*

'I enjoyed reading and judging the entries in the Never Such Innocence Schools' Poetry Competition. The entries were impressive and I congratulate everyone involved on the high standards achieved. It was a pleasure to see how today's young people respond to those terrible events of a century ago.'
HE Dr Daniel Mulhall, Poetry Judge
Ambassador of Ireland

AGES 14–16

## The Fallen Ones

*by Harrison English from Oakwood Park Grammar School, Maidstone*

The fallen ones, they lie alone,
With nothing left, all on their own,
They have strived, and served their country.
But now no one remembers, now they lie solitary.

The young men, only in their teens,
Get trained and given orders and put in their regimes.
They're sent alone, to fight the enemy.
But nothing they could do, no goal they could see.

Now they come home, cut and bruised.
Did they win? Did they lose?
No one knows, they still battle on,
All is darkness, no future seen, no light is shone.

So now the fallen ones lie alone,
War is fearful, and they can't condone
The mindless slaughter, can't be forgot,
And men have died, to bullets hot.

The fallen ones lie alone,
With nothing left, all on their own.

## AGES 14–16

**Disturbed Peace**

*by Melissa Brincat from The Canterbury High School, Canterbury*

AGES 14–16

## Dawn Chorus

*by Annabel Bainbridge from Alleyn's School, London*

A skylark swoops and swings her silver tail,
Below her, sheets of green silk water stir,
A golden ball of life asserts its glow,
And now as then, dawn chorus has begun.
The golden leaves fall softly, softly fall,
Reveal bare branches, winter yet to come,
The silver trunks lean in, whispered exchange,
A secret shared, and snatched, never again.
A moss encrusted, vine entwined, stone cross,
Exuberance of life we owe to them.

## AGES 14–16

### The Personal Effects of William Taylor

*by Scarlett Cameron from Hope Valley College, Hope Valley*

'*I was really impressed with the variety and depth within the work that came in for us to judge from all over the country. There were so many different mediums being used to convey what each student thought of WW1 and how it should be remembered. Some very talented artists out there who I hope will continue to embrace working with visual mediums.*'

Caroline de Peyrecave, Art Judge

**AGES 14–16**

## Harold

*by Gregory Hartley from Alleyn's School, London*

His name is Harold.
He hangs on my brother's wall, a monochrome effigy of what once existed.
The crest emblazoned on his sporran,
Signifies to what he enlisted.

His kilt reaches knee length,
Part of the London Scottish, or Cockney Jocks
Their emblem a collusion of thistles and a saltire
Ready for anything, armed with a dirk tucked into their socks.

He is not my great-grandfather, nor even a relative
On the 30th June 1916, he made his best friend vow,
That if he fell the following day,
He would marry his betrothed and care for her forever and now.

On the 1st July 1916 from this regiment 223 men fell,
Numbers may not signify individuals that someone once called a chum,
Harold was one of these fallen,
And of his life, I can glean from the picture but a crumb.

Williams, Busby, Eckford, Freeman, Heath.
London Scottish lost many Harolds, not just number 4914
Remember the others this year when you lay a wreath.
My great-grandfather, remembered and held to what he swore
My birth made certain by the tragedy, which was the Great War.

**AGES 14–16**

### What happens next?

*by Sean Thackwray from Kingswode Hoe School, Colchester*

What happens next
Will our lips meet again?
I long to feel you
But know in my heart this could be the end!
Are you listening my darling?
There is hate and selfishness,
But I'm only full of love and hope!

AGES 14–16

**Untitled**

*by Lara Tritton from Alleyn's School, London*

2015/16

In our second year we decided to be more ambitious, to work with young people from across the United Kingdom and Crown Dependencies. Never Such Innocence embarked on a series of roadshows – visiting Reading, where we were kindly hosted by Sir John Madejski and the event was attended by Reading FC's Under-21 players; Jersey, Guernsey and the Isle of Man (with the support of Coutts); and Glasgow City Chambers, where we were hosted by the then Lord Provost, Sadie Docherty.

We received entries from as far and wide as Orkney, Northern Ireland, the Channel Islands, New Zealand and Denver, USA (to name but a few!).

When we embarked on our Never Such Innocence journey we wanted to be inclusive, reaching out to communities in all corners of the United Kingdom. For the 2015/16 Competition we piloted a Gaelic strand; the winning entry is printed on page 78.

We partnered with the Royal Navy during the 2015/16 Competition to mark the centenary of the Battle of Jutland, inviting children to submit poetry or art inspired by the only major naval battle of the First World War. We were delighted that NSI winners were invited to play a part in the official Battle of Jutland commemorations taking place across the United Kingdom. Our winning children from England were presented to the Duke of York aboard HMS *Duncan* docked in Canary Wharf whilst our Scottish winners were presented to HRH The Princess Royal and Scotland's First Minister, Nicola Sturgeon at South Queensferry.

Scottish children also featured in a commemorative concert with the Band of Her Majesty's Royal Marines and the German Naval Band on Orkney. Battle of Jutland-inspired winning entries can be found on pages 79–81.

We received 981 entries for the poetry competition and 672 entries for the art competition across all age categories from 112 schools. This amounts to nearly three times as many entries from over twice as many schools compared to the pilot competition.

The 2015/16 Never Such Innocence Competition was supported by the Westminster Foundation, Coutts and the Leathersellers' Company Charitable Fund.

AGES 9–11

## What would they think?

*by Emily Dutson from Perranporth Community Primary School, Perranporth*

I have visited museums; been into a mock trench,
I have tasted the ration packs, and smelt the foul stench,
Of a war that killed more men than my mind can behold.
Of a people so unbelievably strong and so bold.

I have read of the politics – "Ferdinand" rings a bell,
The manoeuvres and battles, all the stories to tell.
Letters home to loved ones never again seen.
The songs sung to keep the spirits up and men keen.
I have heard of the men who saw such horrific sights,
That would chase them through their dreams in the night.

And yet the museum experience of taste, smell, sound and sight,
Cannot bring to me the terrible horror and fright,
Of the 8.5 million who died in the fields,
In the hope a fairer place the world would yield.
But I watch the news sitting next to my mum,
And see the count of people injured, displaced from their homes.
There are millions today affected by wars,
That, people believe, are for a fair and just cause.

We remember the soldiers who died through those years,
They gave up their lives so we could live without fear.
I ask "What would they think of our world today?"
My mum shakes her head, with a look of dismay,
"Oh Emily," she says "Our hope is with you,
your friends and their brothers and their sisters too,
To think of the lessons that millions would give,
To live the life they died for, that they hoped we might live."

## AGES 9–11

### Fuil a' Chogaidh (Blood of War)

*by Mairi Maclennan from Sgoil nan Loch (Lochs School), Isle of Lewis*

AGES 9–11

## Shadows of the Past
*by Louisa Willan from The British Junior Academy of Brussels, Brussels, Belgium*

## AGES 9–11

### Lemon Squeezer Boneyard

*by Pieta Bayley from St Andrew's College Preparatory School, Christchurch, New Zealand*

Boots stomp through mud to slog up a steep Gallipoli cliff
Soldiers' faces are ever grim
Poppies with graceful poise are trampled by feet
Guns fire in a cannon
Bullets dance
People abandon the earth
The souls of many take a starlit staircase from the trenches into the heavens
One shell-shocked soldier longs for home
yet all he sees are skulls wearing lemon squeezers
His mind is troubled and his matted hair as white as the snow that blanketed the dead in their
eternal slumber
A row boat answers his call to a far-flung birthplace Aotearoa
He wakes in his bed crying out for his friends but he hears no reply
They are lost in a hallucination of terrors from a distant land.

*Footnote: The Lemon Squeezer Hat is an icon to New Zealanders of Gallipoli. It was first worn by the Taranaki Rifles Regiment, after being introduced by one of New Zealand's most famous Gallipoli soldiers, Colonel William Malone. Its shape represented a sacred mountain in the area, Taranaki. It was then worn by Malone's Wellington Regiment and was made part of the uniform for the entire New Zealand Infantry Division on 1st January 1916.*

*'I was inspired to write this poem after finding out last year on the 100th year anniversary of the landing at Gallipoli that my Great-Great-Great Uncle Lance Sargeant Arthur Greenwood of the Canterbury Mounted Rifles was killed in action at Gallipoli on the night of 6th of August 1915. He was involved in an attack as part of the beginning of the main assault on Chunuk Bair over the next days. Arthur was 24. He had been given by his father the best horse from his stable called Aladdin, but never got to ride him in war as they couldn't take horses to Gallipoli due to the steep cliffs. We don't know what happened to Aladdin.'*
Pieta Bayley, Second Place Winner

**AGES 9–11**

## The Truce

*by Nuzhath Siddique from Mount Pleasant Junior School, Southampton*

Christmas Eve arrives with hope and misery,
A man stares at his wife.
On this holy night all hatred fades away.
Each battalion was touched with silence like a hand.
Warm smiles spread across the faces of the soldiers.
Men who would shoot, now laugh and sing.
Scarlet blood like festive wallpaper covers the trench walls,
Strange spikey frost on the barbed wire decorates No Man's Land.
Joy gradually spreads through the night,
A gentle lullaby of a chorus broke the silence.
All languages hummed the song to gradually increase into a harmony.
Sadness is no more.
Dawn breaks to silence everyone,
A Londoner turned into a spider
To climb over the wall,
No shrieks of warnings could hold him back,
So others followed suit.
Robins sang as calmly as a river flowing,
His chest was broad and red like Rudolph's nose.
For to friend,
Misery to joy.
Rasping, a German sprinted over No Man's Land.
A battlefield was a pitch,
The ball had longed to be played with and now on Christmas it was possible
Snow as white as a polar bear's coat covers the pitch.
Muddy tracks were painted with the ball.
But happiness can't last forever.
Gun shots made them realise their responsibilities.
Friends to foe and enemies shall remain.

## AGES 9–11

### Dominions Sacrifice

*by Edward Brown from Beechwood Park School, St Albans*

AGES 9–11

## Ruins

*by Katie Hall from Kensworth Church of England Primary School, Kensworth*

**AGES 9–11**

### War Zone

*by Josh Carridge from Onchan Primary School, Isle of Man*

I am Major Carridge I've trained my men to fight,
Today is the day at sundown, we go over the top tonight,
It's gloomy and grey, it doesn't look good,
And in my heart I know there'll be blood
These soldiers I have trained, to honour and protect,
Our country and families we love and respect.
These men miss their children, mothers and wives,
Yet they are here, fighting with their lives.

As I round up my troops, sirens sound out loud,
My men stand before me tall, strong and proud.
I blow on my whistle and wish them good luck,
As bullets start flying, I drop down and duck.
What lies ahead of us, on the other side?
So many before have attempted but died.

Crawling across the battlefield armed, ready and brave,
Please god I beg you, don't send me to my grave.
Flame throwers were launched I commanded fall back!
Fear began to take over, this was a deadly attack.

We cannot be beaten we won't let them win.
I must take control, let the battle begin.
We pulled out grenades, rifles and tanks,
Adrenaline took over as we all closed ranks.

We charge at the enemy, shooting to kill,
Trampling over bodies lying so still.
The stench of death is all around,
Blood and guts cover the ground.

We must push forward and try to forget
That these men have families they love and respect
It's them or it's us, that's what we were told
But men lie here dying, bleeding and cold.
We are opposite sides that are fighting this war
But is it all worth it? What is it for?

Freedom and power is what led us here
Lives lost, blood shed and many a tear.
I ask myself why we cannot be friends
And bring this war to a happy end.
Maybe one day we will all live in peace
But for now war lives on and does not cease.

## AGES 9–11

### Look into my eyes

*by Jay Rintakorpi from Kensworth Church of England Primary School, Kensworth*

Look into my eyes before you fire,
Is this really what you desire?
I'm a man like you. Made from flesh and blood,
Do you want to hide me in the mud?


Look into my eyes before you decide
To send the gas to the other side,
The damage you do will always haunt you,
In the years to come the truth will destroy you

Look into my eyes before you hate me.
Think carefully before you recreate me
Ask yourself: is this right?
Is this worth a soul-crunching fight?

Look into my eyes. Is this a lie?
Do we all have to painfully die?
This war will only drive us apart,
Perhaps only death will make hate depart?

Look into my eyes!

*'Judging the many superb entries to the 2015/16 Never Such Innocence poetry competition was a deeply moving experience. The young poets' empathy with events that happened 100 years ago was humbling.'*
Dr Viv Newman, Poetry Judge

AGES 9–11

## Never Forgotten

*by Mia Staniforth from Elizabeth College Junior School, Guernsey*

## AGES 11–14

### The blind leading the blind
*by Tallulah Pudney from Brighton College, Brighton*

## AGES 11–14

### Waking Nightmare
*by Robyn Beckett from Broxburn Academy, Broxburn*

I thought I had got out.
Escaped the despair that so many great men had fallen prey to
Yet this hell is inside of me.
As I close my eyes this guilt wraps itself around me,
Like the lifeless hands of my fallen comrades,
Their blood caked fingernails leaving invisible bruises on my neck.

Why didn't they take me?
To be cold in the ground is surely more desirable than this life of never-ending torment.

A walking corpse, I stumble through these days lost in the past.
Unable to do anything for myself.
But my heart is always pounding.
The only part of me that seems alive
As my eyes, blinded with tears, gaze out across a gore spattered landscape in my head.

In this waking nightmare, I am all alone.
Unfamiliar faces glaring down at me,
As I crouch in stunned silence,
Surrounded by the corpses of my friends and allies.
Brothers, sons, fathers and husbands:
Each man taken too soon.
Choking on the fumes of gas, drowning.
Drowning in regrets.

*'This is the second time that I have joined a panel of judges and the first time that I kept a poem [Waking Nightmare by Robyn Beckett] by my bedside for so long. I represent the Combat Veteran Players which is made up of ex-service men and women who had suffered from PTSD. This poem has given a clear account of what we are. It has been an honour to be amongst you and a real privilege to be able to learn so much from our young and future generation.'*
Androcles Scicluna, Member of Combat Veteran Players, Poetry Judge

**AGES 11–14**

### The Grieving Parents

*by Beth Warwick from George Heriot's School, Edinburgh*

There they stand
Gazing sorrowfully over the rows of graves
Keeping watch over their sleeping children
Weeping behind their stone facades

The cold has frozen water droplets
To their cheek
Their tears held fast
In the depths of Winter

The snow falls thick
Smothering where they lie
Their boys
Their happy, heroic dead

If they could
Would they break from their stance
Of eternal grief
Bend down to brush the snow from their cribs

Sing them a sweet lullaby
To soothe their fears, quell the horrors
Heal the wounds with a brush of their icy lips
At very least put a name to their bones

But they never will
Instead they grieve
For the hollow loss of life, and hope,
And the sons who paid the price of war

*The Grieving Parents statue stands in Vladslo war cemetery, Germany

AGES 11–14

## Burnt Souls

*by Ryan Shaw from Broxburn Academy, Broxburn*

AGES 11–14

## It's for your country

*by Madeleine Keating from Archbishop Temple School, Preston*

**AGES 11–14**

## Indefinitely Burdening

*by Hannah Owens from Jersey College for Girls, Jersey*

Haunting shadows flit across memory,
Horrors untold and veiled from humanity.
Blurred language in fear of destroyed morale.
Those we lost, who could never voice the truth.

Censored paragraphs deleted in the midst of terror,
Panic at sensitive information reaching the ears of others.
Sorting, modifying each letter with a ruthlessness unmatched.
Those we lost, who could never voice the truth.

Inky black lines scrawl through the cursive,
Deemed unsuitable for public perception.
Instead burdened with a weight alone onwards.
Those we lost, who could never voice the truth.

Families fearfully fingering the torn edges,
Pondering the parts scarred and illegible.
Marching beats drowning out the cries for understanding.
Those we lost, who could never voice the truth.

Deaths disguised under lilting laughter,
Leaving little more than lies and dishonesty.
Crafted stories to lift spirits and relieve their burden.
Those we remember, let us voice their truth.

**AGES 11–14**

### The word behind the war

*by Maddie Macey from Churcher's College, Petersfield*

A holiday,
They said, they said it would be,
A break,
An honour,
A service, you see.

Over by Christmas,
They said it would be,
So quick,
So easy,
And of course we agreed,

So we all ran off,
Guns under arms,
To France,
To Germany,
Where no one was harmed

And, so they said,
Where no one's in danger,
So, if that was true,
Where was John, Joe
Or that stranger?

Sleeping,
They said, they said that they were
Dreaming,
Peaceful,
And all I could do was concur

So as I went over,
And started to snore,
I hoped
That my family
Wouldn't trust the word behind the war.

## When the Whistle Blows

*by Ben Jackson from The Rawlett School, Tamworth*

Over the top, when the whistle blows
Following the river of blood that flows
Bodies strewn all around
Limbs missing never to be found
Death is the only sight
As guns rain down bombs in flight
Shot from the artillery battery
A present from the death factory
Barbed wire rolled like a wreath
Laid on the ground like flowers in grief
We gave our all, we gave the most
Remember us now, as you hear the last post

AGES 11–14

## Europe at War

*by Erica Weiler from Godolphin and Latymer School, London*

AGES 11–14

## A Mother's Journey
*by Lili Beatrice England from Granville Sports College, Woodville*

## AGES 14–16

### No Poppies in the Sand

*by Maeve Loney from St Patrick's College, Ballymena*

In this hot dry river bed
Rest the camels in a row.
They lie in military line
Though they do not have a foe.
Each hapless soldier soon will mount
A most incongruous steed,
And then across hot desert sand
Advance with ardent speed.
Cross-legged on these hump-backed beasts
(As a monument recalls)
The soldiers match their rhythm,
The rises then the falls.

Forward they go to meet the fate
That awaits them on that day.
Will it be death, defeat or victory?
History has yet to say.
There's little glory to be gained
In this theatre of sand;
The greater battles rage and roar
On sea and trench-scarred lands.
That they'll recognise his sacrifice
In the land where he used to live,
Was the silent sigh in a soldier's heart;
There was no more he could give.

*'We examined the image of the James McBey painting, "The Long Patrol: The Wadi"[featured in the Never Such Innocence stimulus materials] which depicts an Imperial Camel Corps patrol which has halted in a wadi, a dried out riverbed in the desert. Maeve was amazed to discover that soldiers actually went to war on camels.*
*In the poetry section Maeve was touched by the poem "Home Thoughts" by Unknown, 1916, as it showed her that even though he was risking his life, this soldier did not expect to receive any honour for it. Also he did not think he would be remembered because of where he had been sent to fight. This prompted her to suppose that a soldier in "The Long Patrol" might have felt this way as well.*
*Maeve has worked hard at researching and crafting her poem and she did it with a lot of enthusiasm and enjoyment. This was in large part promoted by your easily accessible and visually appealing resources, which engaged and sustained her interest throughout.'*
Liz Dempsey, St Patrick's College

**AGES 14–16**

## A Farmer Buries the Dead

*by Mia Nelson from Denver School of Arts, Denver, United States of America*

here in France farmers still till the bloody soil
frequently unearthing the bodies of lost
soldiers in a treasure hunt of flesh.
when asked they say,
*it's always a saddening surprise to find a man.*
*sadder still when we find him in pieces.*

but oh that great wind of war swept wordlessly
across the countryside,
her huge and unjust scythe cutting men like
wildflowers,
burying the bodies lonesome and sallow
to be found by a melancholy farmer
who picks bloody poppies all the days of his
life.

still, beauty has lain her hand across the
French hills,
the grass is tender and spry, moving in the air
green sweetness,
while blue and purple berries dot the rich
black earth.
the lost footprints of soldiers are now spires of
blackberries,
and in their bodies' place is a grand stillness,
the white sky wider for the absences.

the verdant hills and dew smocked cottages
the small, wide eyed crocuses,
the gentle dampness of perpetual fog is only a
shroud over a broken body:
gunshells and trenches masqueraded to be
plots of sugar beets or onions.

but still the aimless unmarked souls of
warriors should wait eternally for the
harvesting-
to be swung over an old farmer's shoulder,
who tells me *he lost his father in the war*
*and has been burying him every day since.*

he leads me behind his house where flowers sit
like tombstones
and shows me a makeshift burial plot.
he tells me *putting the soldiers he finds to rest is*
*the only mourning he allows himself, and,*
*look at how the poppies grow almost in the shape*
*of a uniform, a red shadow for their souls.*

and oh, isn't it lovely
that he calls it a garden
and not a grave.

AGES 14–16

## Tyne Cot Remembered

*by Eloise Fradley from The Rawlett School, Tamworth*

**AGES 14–16**

### Remember!

*by Jessica Rizova from The Astley Cooper School, Hemel Hempstead*

*'I was very impressed by the number and standard of competition entries, and by the way schools had embraced the theme. We had a very hard job indeed but the winners and runners-up stood out for their creativity and thoughtfulness.'*
Rosi Lister, Art Judge
Director North at the Churches Conservation Trust

**AGES 14–16**

## Here I Hold Your Child

*by Olivia Jones from Jersey College for Girls, Jersey*

Here I hold your child,
enclosed in a bump.
listening as we share endless possibilities for the future.

Here I hold your child,
still waiting to arrive
just as you are waiting to depart.

Here I hold your child,
tiny and precious,
her newly-opened eyes yearning
for a glimpse of her father.

Here I hold your child,
attempting basic words into my ear.
It saddens me to hear her speak my name
until you get home.

Here I hold your child,
peaceful and silent,
dreaming the nights away
until you get home.

Here I hold your child,
catching her mother's tears,
not understanding that she has a loving father
that once longed to meet her.

## AGES 14–16

### Far From Home

*by Leah Townsend from King's High School for Girls, Warwick*

## AGES 14–16

### Post war vision

*by Fatima Arman from Hodge Hill Girls' School, Birmingham*

**AGES 14–16**

## Still, We Are Silent

*by Louis Miller from The Norton Knatchbull School, Ashford*

I sit in the rain, the cold wind blows,
The chill passes through me, from my head to my toes.
The bright shells explode, in the sky, above my head,
Still, we are silent, nothing is said.

The guns are blazing, through the night,
As soldiers run, their death in sight.
The bayonets fixed, we'd prefer to stay,
But still, we are silent, there is nothing to say.

Barbed-wire here, the shell's mark there,
My team moves on, but doesn't take care.
That's two lost already, who'll be the third,
But still, we are silent, no-one has stirred.

The tally keeps growing, it's way over five,
I am one of the few still alive.
The sky is black, but approaching dawn
But still, we are silent, as the fires blaze on.

I see the heads of the Jerry in front,
Their rifles are loaded, for them, it's a hunt.
I hear the blast, as the shot hits my chest,
But now, I am silent, as I fall, to rest.

## AGES 14–16

### Remember

*by Charissa Cheong from Wren Academy, London*

I once played football with a man,
Who shot me in the chest.
Exchanged with him a handshake,
He exchanged with me a life.
And now his body lies
beneath the Earth on top of mine,
Under the poppies that they pluck
to remember both of us.

They let them grow over our heads
so they see them instead of us.
A token drop of blood,
Pinned as paper on their chests
so they remember to remember,
Just two minutes of their time,
All I have inside their minds,
And then once again forgotten.

Say a prayer for me,
Remember me.
I ask for your sincerity,
Conscripted me to die, engraved
My name on Heaven's gate.
And here I've found my rest,
With my dearest football friend
And to those we lost to life,
Those whose rest has yet arrived,

All I want to say is
Pray always,
Remember
`Don't forget.

AGES 14–16

## Out of the Darkness

*by Alex Borras from King's High School, Warwick*

## An Cogadh (The War)

*by Hannah Mason from Glasgow Gaelic School, Glasgow*

Tha mi beò fhathast ach ann an cunnart mhòr!
Tha an t-eagal orm, ach tha dòchas agam fhathast.
Tha mi nam sheasamh suas, fuil a' tighinn a-mach às mo chas is mo chean,
Luath, mar an abhainn bheag a' ruith cho luath tron choille gu ceann mo ghàrraidh,
brèagha, gleansach.
"Uilleam! Uilleam! Uilleam!"… tha daoine ag eighadh orm
ach chan urrainn dhomh gluasad.
Roimhe an seo bha mi cho pròiseil gun robh mi sa chogadh
ach a-nis chan eil mi ag iarraidh càil ach mo leabadh agus mo theaghlach!

'S e oidhche dorcha a tha ann a nochd agus tha barrachd marbh na tha beò,
chuala mi bomaig eile agus leis an eagal
dh' eirich mi suas gu socair agus dh' fheuch mi ri gluasad air ais gu an fillteach.
Nuair a ruig mi an fillteach cha robh càil an sin ach pìosan de slèibhtrich agus fiodh.

Thuit mi sìos air mo ghlùinean,
chan eil cùram as an t-saoghal air mo chas an-dràsta.
Choimhead mi mun cuairt air cuirp nan daoine òige.
Chan eil fios agam de nì mi an-dràsta ach feitheimh ri beul na h-oidhche…!

---

*'Hannah Mason's poem gives the impression of having been written in the trenches – stained and bullet–holed! Comparison between the blood pouring out of William's head and a remembered fresh clean stream flowing through his own garden is particularly striking. Details, of debris found in the trench where he seeks shelter, and all the young bodies scattered around, convey a sense of what it must have been like.'*
Aonghas MacNeacail, Gaelic Poetry Judge

## Sea of Souls

*by Grace Batchelor, Kasey Bohee, Liam Bradford, Sonny Chandler, Lacey Crist, Zach Duffy, Alexandria Ellis, Allannah Fuller, Grace Lowe, Samuel Lowe, Billy Mersh, Toby Orpin, Cameron Rawland, Kyle Scanell, Charlie Snell, Harley Upton, Veer Vara, Emma Wiley, Connor Wooley, Lauren Yates, Rhianna Chikwanha from Maundene Primary School, Chatham*

*'Swans class chose to use the Battle of Jutland as a theme for our competition entry because we had been learning about Jack Cornwell. Lots of us have teenage brothers and his story made us realise just how young some of the sailors were in World War One. We also realised that it was not just British sailors who lost their lives. We made the sky to show that this was truly a World War. We used our hands to represent the sea. Swans had lots of ideas for a title, but we chose Sea of Souls because we liked the alliteration and we thought it was quite a sad title. We used collage because it made the subject stick out and we worked on it as a team, just like the sailors in the ships at the battle.'*
A note put together about 'Sea of Souls' by Swans Class at Maundene Primary School

## Scapa Flow

*by Hamish Scott from the Isle of Harris*

The ships arrive
Grey ghosts appearing through the mist
Scapa Flow
Home of Battleship
Longboats of the modern age
It was War
For Scapa Flow

Defences are up
Block ships, booms and barrier
Artillery and Minefield
Prepared for attack
Was Scapa Flow

Entertainment was wanted,
For the bored sailors
A golf course on Flotta
Boxing matches on the ships
Sailors were content
At Scapa Flow

Battle imminent
Combating the Hun
Dogger Bank
And Jutland
The fleet departing
From Scapa Flow

The War…
Won
The German fleet…
Interned
Not without a cost
Thousands of lives lost to the deep.
The fragile peace begins
Scapa Flow

## Bombing all over the place

*by Kayla Muir from Glaitness School, Orkney*

## Jutland

*by Erin Dundas from Orphir Community School, Orkney*

Ships littered the blue deathbed,
The best of the best, wound up dead.
Families are horror-struck,
Many sailors are stuck,
That's not what anyone said.
Mothers anxiously wait for some news,
Then everyone fills the pews,

Children blubbing,
Very troubling,
A quick battle, that's what they said.
The most tragic story ever told,
The Battle of Jutland,
100 Years Old.

## Life in the trenches
*by Martha Potts, age 3*

Wait.
Wait.
Wait.

Fight.
Fight.
Fight.

Die.

*'I wanted to write to say thank you for your online resource which has inspired my eleven year old to write poetry. Little did I know my almost four year old was absorbing it all in too. She came up with the following poem that I promised I'd email to you as she's five years too young to enter the competition!'*
Jacky Potts, Martha's mother

## Poppy Day
*by Mia Eggleton, age 4*

2016/17

Children and young people from around the world continued to move us with their thought-provoking responses to the First World War. For the 2016/17 Competition, we saw record numbers of entries and participating schools, expanding our global reach to include Canada, New Zealand, Malaysia and Romania.

The Competition saw a very successful partnership with the Royal Canadian Legion and their National Poster and Literary Contests, which focus on the theme of Remembrance. This partnership led to six Canadian winning entries (see pages 90, 102, 109, 115, 120 and 121).

During the Roadshow we visited communities in Blackwood, Wales, as part of the Velvet Coalmine Festival organised by Iain Richards; the University of Exeter with kind support from Edson Tiger; Eaton Park,

courtesy of the Grosvenor Estate; the Royal Liverpool Philharmonic with kind support from Dr Tony Harvey; HMS *Iron Duke* docked in Portsmouth, courtesy of Captain Chris Smith; and the Nicholson Institute in Leek, where we were kindly hosted by the Rt Hon Karen Bradley MP, the then Secretary of State for Culture.

In November 2016, Vice Admiral Sir Tim Laurence became our President following the sad death of our founding President, the 6th Duke of Westminster. In the same month, we received a national award for our work during the Centenary from Remember WW1.

We continued to run the poetry competition in English and Gaelic (piloted in 2015/16) and introduced a Welsh language category (see pages 124–125).

In addition, we piloted **Songs of the**

**Centenary** – a global quest for songs inspired by the First World War (see pages 194–199 for full details).

As part of the government's national programme of commemorations, Never Such Innocence was invited to select winning children to attend the Passchendaele 100 events in Belgium. Two British and two Belgian children took to the stage to read their poems, and they were then presented to HRH The Prince of Wales, TRH the King and Queen of Belgium and the British Prime Minster, the Rt Hon Theresa May MP.

For 2016/17 we engaged with children from 157 different schools and educational settings, a 40% increase on 2015/16. A total of 1,289 children entered the poetry competition, and 621 entered the art competition.

The 2016/17 Never Such Innocence Competition was supported by the Department for Culture, Media and Sport, Mappin & Webb and the Leathersellers' Company Charitable Fund.

AGES 9–11

### I stand alone
*by Rebecca Farnfield from South Farnham School, Farnham*

I am the Hornbeam tree, I stand alone
Rooted here on this bloodied throne.
I rule over the dead and I'm testament to their pain,
This wretched war where there's nothing to gain.
I have seen flesh cut like butter, and heard grown men scream,
These harrowing sights haunt my every dream.
I watched them fall, one by one,
The choking gas at the back of their tongue.
I tried to protect them, offering my trunk for strength
But the ceaseless rain of gunfire, meant they couldn't leave the trench.
As my rust coloured leaves fall like tears,
I become a sole survivor of these war torn years.
My roots are embedded with the souls of the dead.
My branches reaching up so their prayers can be said
I'm alone on this meadow, once scarce and rotten,
But my comrades below will never be forgotten.

*'My inspiration came from reading "Monster Calls" by Patrick Ness, the tree in this story has an important message to get across. Giving the tree a voice allowed me to write my poem from a first-hand perspective. This made it more personal and the imagery more powerful and poignant as the tree was actually there living through the pain of war.'*
Rebecca Farnfield, First Place Winner

AGES 9–11

## Invisible Father
*by Leong Tong Yan from Ipoh, Malaysia*

## AGES 9–11

### The Last Salute

*by Ivy Shi from Calgary, Canada*

'Those who accuse today's young people of being self-centred, disengaged and concerned only with their own image, should read the poems submitted to the Never Such Innocence 2017 Poetry Competition. Entering into the horrors of the trenches, the psychological agony of those who waited at home and cognisant of the wounds the war also inflicted on the natural world, the youngsters demonstrated understanding, empathy and emotional intelligence well beyond their tender years.'

Dr Viv Newman, Poetry Judge

## AGES 9–11

### I Will Remember
*by Caitlin Costello from St Charles Borromeo Catholic Primary School, Weybridge*

I sit alone rocking back and forth,
An old man, my skin shrivelled and my eyesight poor,
Dreaming in my own little world and mulling over the life I have lived,
On the outside ancient and dead, the inside whizzing and
whirling with memories of the past enclosed inside my mind,
I remember,

We march off into the welcoming horizon,
Fooled by its sense of safety,
Our eyes so young and shining,
Unaware of the fire about to set them alight,
Young boys not wise enough to understand our own weakness,
I remember,

Wading through the slushing mud,
We sing to keep our spirits from this tragic reality,
Our minds back home in our warm beds, silent and safe,
Our hearts with those we left behind patiently awaiting our return,
Those left praying that we will come back untouched and our souls unshattered,
I remember,

My heart pounding and my heart beating,
A blanket of smoke falls around us encasing us inside death's jaws as we cough and splutter,
There's a symphony of guns and explosions ringing in my ears,
deafening me and pulling me to the ground in fright,
I am shocked at each breath I take for each symbolizes my still beating heart,
I remember,

I see a soldier opposite me, an enemy, therefore a victim of my shot,
But then I look past his uniform and into his pleading eyes,
My mind urges my hand towards the trigger, but my heart wavers,
The man is no different to me, lost in the confusion of war and hiding from the
uncertainty of his future,
I pull my gun back and we exchange glances, a friendship not to be expanded but not
non-existent
I remember,

Remaining bodies lie still scattered across the ground in a pool of red,
noble blood shed for the future of their countries,
We stand hand in hand with spirits of friends and relatives lost in battle so bloody
for the freedom of others,
But now I am back in the present sitting on the fields where my life was almost lost,
The memories these  fields hold are hidden with seas of poppies showing hope left
from the hearts of the soldiers who made it out,
I will remember.

## AGES 9–11

### A Child's View of the War

*by Francesca Clarke from Portsmouth High Junior School, Portsmouth*

Who will read me a story at bedtime?
Now that daddy has gone.
Who will help me with my homework?
Now that daddy has gone.
Who will make me laugh when I'm down?
Now that daddy has gone.
Who will help me mend my toys?
Now that daddy has gone.
Who will take me to school?
Now that daddy has gone.

Mummy, where has daddy gone?
Please tell me mummy, where has he gone?

*'I was immediately overwhelmed by the quantity, then by the variety – and the quality. Such original approaches, such empathy and understanding – and in such young writers! I brought some of the poems home with me. I wanted to have the opportunity to read and re read them.*
*I am still looking at these poems – and not all of them have actually been placed as prize winners. There are only a limited number of prize positions. But every child who entered a poem is already a winner because these children have had the chance to learn about – and learn from – an unparalleled time in our history.'*
Michaela Morgan, Poetry Judge
Poet and Children's Writer

AGES 9–11

## Let's Make Art Not War

*by Calvin Metcalfe from St Keyna Primary School, Bristol*

## AGES 9–11

### Peace

*by Beatrice Haynes from Elizabeth College Junior School, Guernsey*

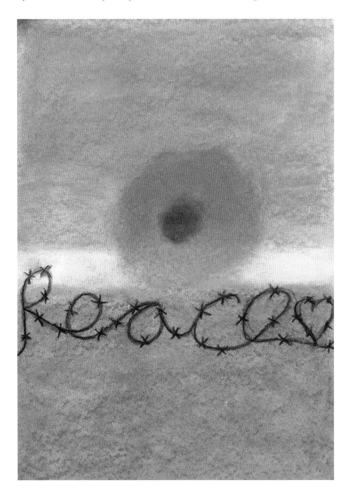

AGES 9–11

## 1914

*by Ethan Edwards from Libanus Primary School, Blackwood*

**AGES 9–11**

## The Stone Soldier
*by Ruby Townsend from Thrupp Primary School, Stroud*

The soldier of everlasting faith
They call him the war memorial
And his only friends are the crosses

Never stopping
Never resting
Full with belief he waits for peace to come

A forever lasting pillar of hope
Feel stuck to the ground
A guard protecting all the lost souls of the past

Stands proud and straight
Like waiting for his next order
Wanting you to know one thing
The world depended on him and his pals.

AGES 9–11

## When the war is over

*by Daisy Powell from Shenington Church of England Primary School, Shenington*

When the war is over,
The earth shall fall to sleep.
Dreaming of long forgotten ground,
Still ringing with retreat.
When the war is over,
The flag of white will fall,
Painting the graves with hope and peace
Where poppies now stand tall.

*'The children enjoyed writing these and I was very proud of their thoughtful independent work. Writing for a purpose and an audience really spurred the children on. Thank you for providing this opportunity and inspiring such young children to learn more about history.'*
Shirley Turner, teacher at Rotherfield Primary School

**AGES 11–14**

### Why?

*by Erin Longley from Holy Trinity Church of England Secondary School, Crawley*

Where have all the birds gone? Why can't I hear their song?
They've gone, my darling…gone. All you hear now is the blast of the gun.

Where have all the flowers gone? Why can't I smell their scent?
They've gone, my darling…gone. That's the stench of fear and death.

Where have all the boys gone? Why can't I hear their laughter?
They've gone, my darling…gone. All you hear now are the cries of men.

Where has the warm sun gone? Why am I so cold?
It's gone, my darling…gone. These are dark, dark days.

Where has my life gone? Why can't I see your face?
You've gone, my darling…gone. Rest, rest in peace.

**AGES 11–14**

## We Are Making a New World
*by Cameron Hair from Hampton School, Hampton*

## AGES 11–14

### They shall not grow old…
*by Yiwei Ni from Vancouver, Canada*

*'It was inspirational and a pleasure to judge the NSI Art competition for 2017. I was very impressed with the way in which WW1 was depicted through art and to such a high standard. It made our decisions all the more difficult! Well done to everyone that took part.'*
Flight Sergeant Gill Malam, Art Judge
Ministry of Defence

**AGES 11–14**

## Snapshot
*by Grace Miller from Gumley House Convent School, Isleworth*

Gun in hand, heart in throat.
Tears in eyes, blood on coat.
Targets see, friends are not.
Poppies grow, bodies rot.
The man just killed, that could've been you.
Two innocents fighting, different leaders, same view.
Wanting a loved one, a meal to devour.
A cause of war from the want of power.
A crumpled letter, a tear down face.
A living son, a relief, but not an embrace.
Three more weeks, then hopefully home.
A steaming hot dinner, his chair a throne.
Boat trips awaiting, bags soon to be packed.
Letters sent and picture intact.
One bullet shot, that's all it took
For the mother to weep and the meal not cooked.
A boat with empty seat, his throne no heir,
No embrace, just a picture, framed with care.
His story not rare, like thousands he met.
For all those killed, lest we forget.

## AGES 11–14

### A Ring
*by Emily Russell from The Royal School, Hindhead*

My love, my soul mate, my life,
Left to go to the bleak battle fields of France,
To fight for his country, England,
His bloody, tear stained jacket returned but not him,
His smell lingers on the collar as I pull the coat to my face,
I reach into his pocket, my fingers grasp something cold and metal,
A clatter on the floor,
A ray of sunshine
There breaking through the grey gloom of my heart glimmers a ring
But I never new he felt this way,
Why would he do such a thing for a girl like me?

*'This competition was focused on a subject students are interested in, and allowed them to express this in a variety of media. It really allowed students to get involved in the topic without being made to write an essay! I also really liked having past winners to show as examples and a really good resource pack available.'*
Sarah Penny, Teacher at Alton Convent School

**AGES 11–14**

## We are the Dead
*by Honey Marshall from Alton Convent School, Alton*

AGES 11–14

## The Homecoming

*by Poppy Methold from Ryde School with Upper Chine, Isle of Wight*

**Forget me not**
*by Eloise Hunt from Claverham Community College, Battle*

So many men, they all fight as one,
Yet each man, he stands alone,
This is war, not time for fun,
They're so far from home,

On the way there's time to think,
What to prepare for, stomachs sink.
They miss their loved ones left at home,
But for now these lands they'll roam.

Each step they take is closer to death,
It's getting harder to walk, they can't catch their breath,
The idea is burned deep into their mind,
That their lives so easily away have signed.

All are scared of what is to come,
Words unspoken, they're all feeling numb.
There is a pain they must all carry and bear,
And a loss they all must equally share,

All the things they should have said,
There are bombs underfoot, watch where you tread,
In a land full of fear, brothers they fall,
All men will lose, not one man stands tall.

## AGES 11-14

### Three Koi Fish

*by Tom Yeadon from Blundell's School, Tiverton*

3 Koi fish floated along a stream made up of mud;
Fear, Disease and Hope

Fear was an ebony death,
Swiftly swimming, seeping into the minds of soldiers
Long elegant fins scraping along the walls
Plummeting into the darkest corners of consciousness
Nestling down to forge the chains of worry

Disease was slender,
Darting between the gaps of carelessness
Silvery-white hues blinded all who hosted the creature
As teeth sink in, mould, death and suffering all appear
Once finished, it leaps onto another pathetic spirit

Fingers tremble as Fear seizes control.
Keeping it a hostage
Shrieks paint the sky with bright bursts
Crimson cascading from wounds
Disease penetrates the locks we place around life
Releasing it unto a world beyond us

Then there was Hope
Orange glimmers glide over scales, a beauty to behold
It floated into hearts, leaving Joy and Love empty

Only to vanish as swiftly as it came
Haunting another victim with the lie of false hope

AGES 11–14

## Lest We Forget
*by Grace Gao from Ottawa, Canada*

## AGES 14–16

### Dear Ivy

*by Hannah Owens from Jersey College for Girls, Jersey*

Dear Ivy,

I hope our little Johnny is well.
    Bound in formality, the tear brushed from the page.
    Curl the pain inside the hand clenched around pen and ink,
    Words I cannot say and must hold against my mind;
    Take to my grave, wherever I shall at last lie.

    A child we brought into a world where I wish he could never need walk.
    Hold him dear to your heart, Ivy, for I've seen a world that would destroy him.
    I live in that world each day and I don't think my heart can beat to love anymore.

I truly miss you and I look forward to seeing you again.
    Could you love and forgive the hands that have killed?

My dearest, a moment does not pass when I do not think of you.
    The war flickering behind my eyes,
    Memories echoing in my dreams and ringing the tolling bells in my ears,
    The sighing of men in their final moments.
    The screams, the final screams, those screams that you can never shut out.

I am going to fight in this war, win this war for you and our Johnny.

Ivy, tell him of me, would you? Tonight as you cradle him.
    Remind him that once you married me, and felt at peace in my arms-
    That I was a good man that never raised his hand against another.
    Oh, remind me that I once… once was something else.

Tell Johnny- father'll be home soon.
      A father he can never rely on, one he must turn from in shame.
      I've become all I feared, all you never dreamt of;
      A mirror of cowardice that lurks in the sombre abyss of his mind. Alone.

As they say, Ivy, this war'll be over by Christmas.
      I wade each day through the murky depths of lies,
      Falling around me, to settle alone upon the fields.
      That's what they say, although for whom I am not sure;
      Do you wait with impatience to hold a scarred one sooner?
      Do I long to see the disappointment upon your face?

Yours with love,
      If inside me there is anything left that I may call love,
      As pure that I could dare to bestow upon you.
      I made you mine, and yet now what can I return?
      A father I am not fit to be,
      As your husband I could not look you in the eye and hold your gaze.

      I'm broken.

Your Samuel.

      Help me.

AGES 14–16

## Hidden Grief
*by Anna Horwich from Uppingham School, Uppingham*

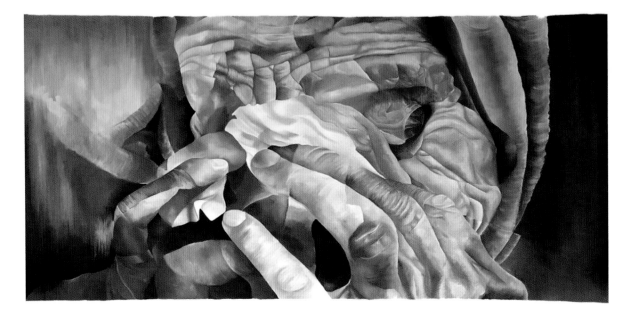

## In The Dark

*by Liam Walsh from Claverham Community College, Battle*

As the light of the grey day faded to leave,
only total darkness,
the snow began to fall so thick you'd freeze,
until the lamps,
were lit with matches held by shaking fingers,
illuminating dull,
the trenches filled with near-dead ringers.

The eve was cold, t'was as if a cloak,
laid by the north and south,
had stifled all life, but left the hoax,
that life still existed in the devil's mouth.

No man should be made to wade through mud,
snow and swathes of bodies rotten,
no man should suffer the lack of life's bud,
but these men knew hell, their comforts forgotten,
they followed the orders of generals on high,
'for King and Country' was the supposed reason,
to fight against humans, their very own kind,
for to do anything else would be considered treason.

These men, who knew the secret hell,
did not question.
The cyclic blast of shell after shell,
seemed to herald a bastion.

*Continued...*

These men carried their equipment and weapons,
but these were naught compared to the burden,
of their duty, they knew it ended in Heaven,
the place which they'd earned in service for certain.

As for the light faded dim,
they knew their fate was sealed,
yet they accepted the fact, however grim,
and pushed on through the battlefield.

As the light of day faded low,
they waited for the mark,
when they heard the whistle blow,
they greeted death as a friend in the dark.

*'The standard of writing across all age groups was so high that choosing the final winners was no easy task…*
*Some of the most heart-rending pieces portrayed the experience of war from a child's perspective, while others*
*captured the essence of soldiering so effectively that I found it difficult to believe that the words were penned by*
*21st century teenagers.'*
Major (Ret'd) Barry Alexander, Poetry Judge

## AGES 14–16

### Love to our Country/ Lest we Forget

*by Jude Brian Derla  from St Brieux, Canada*

AGES 14–16

## The woman who fought
*by Esme Fergusson from King's High School for Girls, Warwick*

AGES 14–16

## Pin Drop

*by Rosina Griffiths from Uppingham School, Uppingham*

The last echoes of the bugle call
Have been swallowed by the deafening silence
That envelops us all.
We are thrust into a time unfamiliar to us,
To witness the stolen youth of a generation.

Any day they could be gone,
Brother, Father, Husband, Son.
The ones they love must stay at home.
Mother, Sister, Daughter, Wife,
Must face the prospect of life…
Alone.

Letters float across the sea,
Brimming full of love and hope
In order to hide their fears.
Only some come limping back,
Whilst others bring news greeted only
By tears.

The red flower falls and
The tiny clamour of the pin's head shatters the silence.
The reveille sounds,
The longing lament of those who lost,
Lost so much more than their youth.

## AGES 14–16

### Till I Hear Your Footsteps

*by Laura Crawley from St Patrick's College, Ballymena*

Come close my mother Nancy,
And give me your blessing free.
Say you're proud of your soldier son,
As I take tender leave of thee.

It's time to right old wrongs, we're told,
In the world I'll play my part.
They say there's glory to be gained,
So I'll go with a hopeful heart.

Men are leaving from their great estates,
And from many a cottage small.
Our hearts are stirred up by the cause,
Together we've answered the call.

My cousins John and Joseph
Have already signed up to go,
Young Bernard awaits me at the gate,
So I must not be slow.

Mother you know the world is wide
But if on this farm I'd keep;
I'd live in dreary drudgery
As I'd plough and sow and reap

Yet I'll dream of the lanes, where in summer I strolled,
Hedged with roses, wild and sweet.
The lark's loud song as I cut the corn
In the field where two rivers meet.

And I'll miss our granite mountains grey,
That sweep to swirling seas;
The green glens where vanilla gorse
Scents the spring time breeze.

Of victory we are certain, dear one,
So I'll come back to your fireside bright,
When there's glistening holly on the mantle shelf.
I'll be home by Christmas night.

Goodbye my darling Daniel,
How my heart with grief does burn.
I'll place a candle on the window sill
Each night till you return.

It will glow there through the dark times,
For my pride, my youngest boy.
Till I hear your footsteps at my door
My heart will not know joy.

AGES 14–16

## Lest We Forget Their Sacrifices
*by Jiade Guo from Scarborough, Canada*

AGES 14–16

## Remember the Fallen

*by Jennifer Boadway from Viking, Canada*

**AGES 14–16**

### I Am

*by Rida Khan from The Tiffin Girls' School, Kingston upon Thames*

I am a mother protecting her child,
I watch him sell newspapers down the lane,
Although on the outside he seems beguiled,
I can see how his eyes hold so much pain.
I am a wife waiting for her husband,
Every letter he sends me gives me hope,
For I fear for his life every second,
And sometimes I find it hard not to mope
I am a sister serving the Women's Land Army,
I work with the others on the farm everyday,
Although to some this concept strikes as smarmy,
At least we are now almost getting equal pay.
I am a woman at war,
At war with myself, at war for our lives,
And at war for our country,
Do not forget that I am waiting, waiting, waiting,
For the return of peace.

'It is extremely important that we look at our shared history and commemorate it. We need to look to the past in order to be able to understand where we are today, to be able to shape our future. It is an amazing thing, that Never Such Innocence and the children are doing, to make sure we learn the lessons of the past.'

Imam Asim Hafiz, Islamic Advisor to the Ministry of Defence

## Dà Bhalach as an Eilean (Two Boys on the Island)

*by Hamish Scott from the Isle of Harris*

Dà bhalach as an eilean
A' seasamh air a chidhe
A' feitheamh ris a' bhata
Airson an giulain gu cogadh
'S iad air bhoil.

Dà bhalach as an eilean
Ann an campa an airm
Gun fhios mun chràdh
A tha roimhpe
S'iad saorsnail.

Dà bhalach as an eilean
Anns an trainnse
A' fuireach ris an ath shreath de nàimhdean
Is am bas nan sealladh
Is iad fo iomagain.

Dà bhalach as an eilean
A sabaid an Caisear
Feumar seasamh daingeann
Am measg na feadhainn a tha leòinte, tinn
Is iad brònach.

Aon bhalach as an eilean
A dol dhachaigh fa dheòigh
'S e caoidh a charaid
A' thuit as a bhlar
'S e tùrsach

Aon ghaisgeach as an eilean
A tilleadh dhan' a bhlàr-chatha
Aig a cheart uair seo, gun ghunna a' losgadh
Gun èigheachd s'gun chràdh
'S e meòrachadh; "Carson a thachair seo?"
Carson? Carson? Carson?

*'Da Bhalach is neatly structured, with a clear, but not rigid, sense of rhythm. Repetition of the first line, which changes with the sad turn of events, both drives the poem and adds to its emotional impact.'*
Aonghas MacNeacail, Gaelic Poetry Judge

## Yr Enaid Byw (My Living Soul)

*by Mari Wyn Jones from Ysgol Maes Garmon, Mold*

Disgwyl arswyd, disgwyl angau,
Disgwyl anfad ac anafau;
Wedi oriau o ddiflastod,
Brwydr waedlyd ddaw'n annatod.

Colli hyder a cholli ffydd,
Colli gobeithion i fy hun
Pan ddaw'r gelynion dros y bryn
A ninnau'n sefyll yno'n syn.

Profi'r gwaed a phrofi'r gwallgof
Profi'r pryder ddaw yn angof;
Yr arfau'n rhuo hyd y wawr:
Gwn mai uffern yw fy myd nawr…

Cofio'r bechgyn, cofio ffrindiau,
Cofio'r hunllef o flinderau;
Mi gefais innau ras fy Nuw—
Ond marw bydd fy enaid byw.

---

'*…the power of the poem is that the meaning shines through the structure and, indeed, the rhythmic pattern itself adds dimension to the message. The theme is fear, death, injury, misery and the loss of hope. But there are other powerful emotions here – the sense of futility, of anger and, of course, the depiction of war itself, the nightmare of the noise. The language is carefully crafted, the punctuation is accurate and effective…*'
Professor Sir Deian Hopkin, Welsh Poetry Judge
Chair of Wales Remembers-Cymru'n Cofio 2014-19 and Adviser to the First Minister of Wales

---

2017/18

The 2017/18 Competition was the biggest and most successful of our four Centenary Competitions, with over 40 countries and territories participating across five continents. Our final Centenary Competition received 7,136 entries, more than a threefold increase on our 2016/17 Competition, from as far and wide as India, Germany, Canada, South Korea, Rwanda and Greece.

During the Roadshow we visited communities at numerous exciting and prestigious venues across the UK and Europe, including Birmingham Council House, the Ulster Museum, Thessaloniki City Hall, RAF Valley, RAF Odiham, Edinburgh Castle, Sunderland Minster, RAF Leeming, CWGC Head Office, Hattingen Comprehensive School, RAF Lossiemouth, the Guildhall and the RAF Museum, Hendon. Our special guests included Prime Minister Theresa May, Chief of the Air Staff Sir Stephen Hillier, and Islamic Advisor to the Ministry of Defence Imam Asim Hafiz.

Our 2017/18 Competition featured two special bonus strands, **Thank You** and **War in the Skies**. In partnership with The Royal British Legion we invited young people to pay tribute and say Thank You to the First World War generation. It was an opportunity for a creative expression of appreciation and gratitude – winning works may be found on pages 170–179. And together with RAF100 we encouraged children to consider the war in the skies as part of their contribution to mark 100 years since the formation of the world's first independent air force – winning works may be found on pages 180–193. Prizes included the opportunity to take part in the unique RAF100 flypast over Horse Guards Parade in London.

For the 2017/18 competition, we partnered with Glasnevin Trust in Dublin and were delighted to receive a host of excellent entries from Ireland to the competition. Working together with the Glasnevin Trust we are proud to celebrate the hard work and creativity of children from across the island of Ireland as they play their part in the Children's Centenary Legacy along with their peers around the world.

Our **Salonika Remembers** project – in partnership with the British Council, the British Embassy in Greece, the Commonwealth War Graves Commission (CWGC) and the Museum for Macedonian Struggle – invited schools across Greece to visit and explore their local CWGC cemeteries and respond to this experience creatively. This project produced three 2017/18 Competition winners, whose entries may be found on pages 131, 137 and 152.

All entries submitted through Salonika Remembers were exhibited at the Museum of Macedonian Struggle, which was visited by the British Ambassador to Greece, HE Kate Smith, and winning children featured in the official commemorations at Doiran Cemetery in the presence of HRH The Duke of Kent.

We extended our English, Gaelic and Welsh strands, inviting entries in ALL languages. A total of 3,850 children entered the poetry competition, 2,482 entered the art competition, and 772 participated in Songs of the Centenary; across all age categories from 712 different schools and educational settings.

The 2017/18 Never Such Innocence Competition was supported by The Royal British Legion, National Lottery funding from the Big Lottery Fund, the Department for Digital, Culture, Media and Sport, RAF100 and the Leathersellers' Company Charitable Fund.

**AGES 9–11**

## The Poppy

*by Marat Bilalov from London*

I waited many years in vain
For blood to water my roots with pain

The heavy steps and drops of blood
Had churned the soil from grass to mud

I heard it all from underground
My hiding place had lain unfound

Until the jolt of grief and death
Innocent men, their final breath

When guns fell silent and cries had ceased
All was quiet, my fields at peace

Barren lands and trenches deep
A resting place for those who sleep

Soul and seed as one we grew
A little seedling, pushing through

I was the first to stand up tall
To weep in pain for those who fall

My comrades followed soon behind
To give a reason to remind

Petals stained a bloody red
The tears that many mothers shed

Leaves so full of hopes and dreams
A field of crops that thrives and gleams

A poisoned stud so small and black
Our loved ones never welcomed back

We are forever in their debt
A field of souls lest we forget

AGES 9–11

## Air Raid

*by Konstantinos Kostopoulos from 13th Primary School of Kalamaria, Kalamaria, Greece*

*'Konstantinos heard about the First World War for the first time and he was very interested in the way soldiers fought (trenches, artillery, air raids). His inspiration was to create a war scene that would depict planes bombarding over the trenches. That would be a very usual scene for the First World War. He used charcoal so as to create a black and white scene referring to the past.'*
Stella Tziafeta, Teacher at 13th Primary School of Kalamaria

## AGES 9–11

### Lest We Forget

*by Sonja Csik from St Michael Catholic Academy, Thornhill, Canada*

AGES 9–11

## For a Horse
*by Matthew Heaney from Lough View Integrated Primary School, Belfast*

Four fast hooves clip, clip, clopping
Fine high head nodding, bobbing
Smartly stepping, forward going
Wind wafting, soft mane flowing

Long legs lithely trot, trot, trotting
Following orders, slowly stopping
Heavy sack slinging, broad back breaking
Once more starting, muscles aching

Frightened heart thud, thud, thudding
Big brown eyes stinging, streaming
Terrible noises, screaming, moaning
Poisoned air gasping, groaning

Sinews burning, throb, throb, throbbing
Deep in mud, struggling, straining
Smells so dreadful, shocking, stinking
Breathing harshly, downward sinking

Strong neck tensing, pull, pull, pulling
Not giving up, snorting, striving
Journey completed, panting wheezing
Heavy load lifted pain now easing

Heroic war horse – worth remembering!

**AGES 9–11**

### Ready

*by Ryan Reed from Walkergate Community School, Newcastle upon Tyne*

They thought they were ready for anything.

Deranged trees dancing in the midnight breeze.

Squishy, clumping mud traps innocent feet.

The cloudy water glistens in the light.

Water, like glass, reflecting destruction.

Rusting barbed wire stands far from old ladders.

An angry shell whistles as it flies past.

The orange metal is smashed and flung.

A furious wind growls in the night.

Decomposing stretchers lie in the trench.

Rows of dead trees stand silently like lamp-posts.

Beyond the night sky, the men turn their backs.

They thought they were ready for anything.

AGES 9–11

## In Flanders Fields
*by Kacper Machnik from Leighton Academy, Crewe*

AGES 9–11

## Untitled

*by Kedaton Campbell from the United States of America*

## AGES 9–11

### Thank You

*by Anastasia Basta from the 3rd Primary School of Eleftherio-Kordelio, Thessaloniki, Greece*

To those who fought with allies

To those who felt alone

To those who lost their lives

To those who came back home

To those who suffered for freedom

To those of early youth

To those who left a widow

To those who nursed the dreadful wounds

To those iron birds, high in the sky

To those working hands that stayed behind

To all those souls, full of valour

A great "THANK YOU"

in poppy's pure red colour.

*'Judging the "Never Such Innocence" poetry competitions has been amongst the most rewarding and frustrating of my Centenary commitments. Rewarding due to entrants' impressive empathy with the horror and the suffering of those pain-filled years. Frustrating because not every poem could be a winner – at times, debates amongst the judges were spirited! Through the Children's Centenary Legacy, NSI has ensured that 21st century children from around the world will keep "faith with those who die[d]".'*
Dr Viv Newman, Poetry Judge

## AGES 9–11

### Death Will Find You
*by Holly Brady from the City of London School for Girls, London*

Oh Death,
Please do not claim me
Into your abyss of perpetual darkness
Where souls forever wander, alone
Not knowing that the world
Goes on without them.
I know that I am at your doorstep
With every step towards the battlefield.
Every step that could be my last.

You are not welcome here, oh Death,
Though you take us; unwilling as we are.
Fighting valiantly for our country,
But every bullet is your hand,
Reaching out to take us,
And you delight as our eyes go glassy,
As our life blood drains away into the soil,
Where many have fallen,
And will fall in the war torn days and years to
come.

I do not want you, oh Death,
Let me live, for my country.
But all is the same to you-
British or German, Russian or Austro-
Hungarian.
Whether I was their target or on the side,
I pray for those who have succumbed to you
clutches.
Lucky though I have been,
I know now that when I open my eyes,
I will find you.

*'It is with great pleasure that I would like to congratulate Holly Brady from the City of London School for Girls based in my constituency on her success in the 2017/18 Never Such Innocence Poetry Competition. Her poem "Death Will Find You" is an exceptionally well written piece and captures the very essence of what so many serving on the Western Front, and indeed across the world, would have felt and suffered. To have such emotive and poignant words come from someone so young a century on is quite an achievement. I am sure that Holly's literary skills will further flourish elsewhere in the future.'*
Rt Hon Mark Field MP (Cities of London and Westminster)

AGES 9–11

## The Face of War
*by Anna Potocnik Hahonina from London*

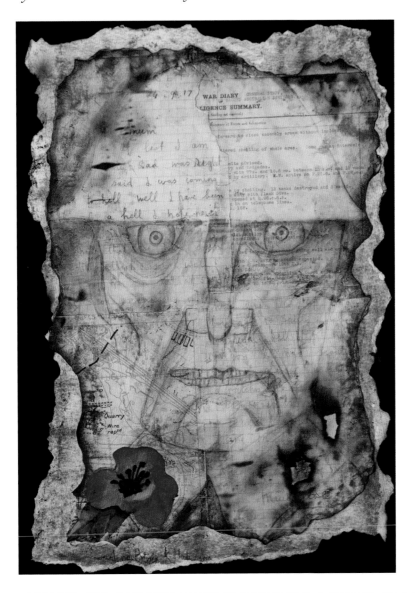

## AGES 11–14

### The Indian Soldier*

*by Jasleen Singh from Bristol Grammar School, Bristol*

Home is where the heart is
I heard a British Soldier say that here
If that is true my love
My home is a long, long way from here

My heart is under the mango tree
Where its sweet blossoms smile almost as wide as me
Instead shells are pouring like the rains in the monsoon
Only we don't know for certain that these will ever stop

My heart is wondering somewhere far away from this God forsaken land
Where night is never silent and stars are never seen
Our richly spiced food is traded for a cold hard bread
It impales my teeth like the bullets struck in the walls back home

My heart longs to fly away from here and join the flock of migrating birds
They are escaping the smoke that plumes like wispy ghosts
For a brighter land with silks of red, yellow and orange
And a sun that beams just as vividly

My heart longs for freedom, freedom and peace
I have a wish that my children can live in a world with more justice than me
I do this for a promise, my love
A promise to own the soil beneath our feet

My heart belongs to the corn fields
And a warm breeze running free
Instead the corpses cover the fields
Like sheaves of harvested corn

My heart belongs to the children, hold them tight my dear
Tell them whatever happens, Papa will always be near
Tell them funny stories, make them laugh from ear to ear
I shall be able to hear their laughter, even from a place as far as here

Our hearts long to sing
Instead they are silenced
Hidden amongst the millions of white crosses surrounding our graves
Why?

We too gave our all when it came to the cry of the fight

*This poem is to commemorate all the 1.3 million Indian Soldiers who came to an unknown country to fight for the British during World War 1.*

## AGES 11–14

### Behind each man

*by Morrigan Atherton Forshaw from Albany Academy, Chorley*

AGES 11–14

## The Torch
*by Ziteng Cai from Alliance Art Academy, Canada*

The Torch
To you from failing hands we throw
The torch; be yours to hold it high.

## AGES 11–14

### Left Behind

*by Molly Leamon from St Edward's Royal Free Ecumenical Middle School, Windsor*

Grey-haired, lonely, lost in thought
Silent, rocking back and forth
Knitting socks he'd never wear
So young he died, no life to spare

No photographs above the flames
Just memories of sunlit days
They were so young they had not guessed
What horrors soon would break the jest
Of glory, pride and honoured deaths
Not frozen toes and rasping breaths

Grey-hair, rocking in her chair
Knitting socks he'd never wear

*'War is such a complex issue and, sadly, one that far too many of our young people continue to have direct experience of. We have so much to gain from the creative reflections of these young people. These poems can make us think and feel differently about a history we thought we knew. It was a privilege to be part of the judging process.'*
Cheryl Moskowitz, Poetry Judge

## Stones

*by Lucy Albuery from The Portsmouth Grammar School, Portsmouth*

You'll say you'll remember,
And I'll trust you that you'll try,
As you stand in Cathedrals,
Wearing pathetic, paper flowers.
You'll remember a few numbers,
Maybe a few names
Or just those graves you once saw on a school
trip.
But for all you do to not let us fade away You
can't bring yourself to apprehend, that We're
already gone.

Never another noise will shake us,
Yet through the silence, blares
Rows and rows of what we became:
White rectangles, tattooed
With some numbers and a name.
A name that you claim to enshrine,
And numbers you pretend to have meaning to
you.
But they're not what matters.
Because all that did has withered,
Into the cold soil we sleep.

You don't know who I was,
So how do you insist you remember
What you never knew?
I am love
I am fear
I am all that I've lost
And all the scars that defined me,
All I gave
and all I took.
I am hope
I am loss
All the tears that escaped.
I am what I showed the world
And all I hid from it, too.
All I am you will never know
By a name and some dates.

You don't remember me.
You remember a stone.

## AGES 11–14

### La vie derrière les mots/Life behind words

*by Lou Gesse from College du val d'Ornois, Gondrecourt-le-Château, France*

'For families, letters were the only way of "feeling" the presence of the soldiers. It was thus possible to stay in contact with them and with shared memories. This link was all the more important as the families of the soldiers were not sure of seeing them again. Letters could help people hold out hope in life.'
Lou Gesse, Third Place Winner

AGES 11–14

## Home, Sweet Home
*by Breanna Hogue from Art School of Olga Nazarkina, Deep River, Canada*

## AGES 11–14

### Am I Not

*by Jasmine Surif from Malborough College, Iskandar Puteri, Malaysia*

I am a woman, and I wish to serve
What difference does it make
If I am not a boy, a man, nor a husband?
"No," they advise me,
"You must not fight!
It's too risky for you,
Stay a housewife."

Why is that so? Why should that be?
Am I weak? Am I fragile?
Am I not what my country needs?
Should women forge weapons, yet stay away
While men handle them, and succumb to the pain?

I am a woman, and I wish to serve
If a human has the right to live
The right to protect
The right to fight
So should I.
Because I'm human too,
Am I not?

Yet here I am
Oppressed, behind the frigid window bars
Watching, with a heavy heart,
As the footsteps of my beloved
On the dried, rusty leaves
Slowly fades away

As the foul balls of toxic rise into the air
As one by one, men of all nations lie lifeless
On the once-green grass
As I bear the harrowing reality
That my loved ones are no more

Shattered and broken, I ponder once more
What difference I could have made.
Instead of remaining and crafting the guns,
I'd have battled for justice, jubilant that we've won.

But here I am, alive.
Basking in the light of victory
Drowning in tears of misery
Because I am a woman.
Am I not?

## AGES 11–14

### We Shot the Dreamers

*by Lili Fairclough from Mossbourne Victoria Park Academy, London*

We ask why we don't move forward
Why our future is stuck in the past
Why every war we wage
Is somehow never the last

The ones who can tell us
Are the ones who are gone
Their lights were extinguished
In battles like the Somme

How to fix our shattered world
Scarred. Everywhere.
With wounds that will not heal
And people unaware

For they know not what is missing
For they know not who has been killed
For they know not the many faces
Whose last sights were those fateful fields

We will not find salvation
Till we look back to the past
To the Dreamers that we shot
In the war that was our 'last'

## AGES 11–14

## Miners

*by Sam Davidson from Hampton School, Hampton*

'I wish to congratulate Sam Davidson on being a runner up in this art competition. A truly incredible achievement, especially as there were 7,000 entries from around the world. Sam is not only a fantastic artist but he has also successfully highlighted a much neglected aspect of the First World War, that of the immense bravery and sacrifice of the men who took part as miners building an extensive networks of tunnels behind Allied lines to allow the undetected movement of men and supplies.'
Rt Hon Sir Vince Cable MP (Twickenham)

## AGES 14–16

### Eyes Wide Shut but Mind Wide Open

*by Vasko Stamboliev from Arsakeio Senior High School of Thessaloniki, Thessaloniki, Greece*

'To create this piece of art, I was inspired by the absence of light caused by the catastrophe and atrocities in war. I imagined the soldiers that bravely fought against all those monstrosities with their eyes wide shut, too scared to open for fear of facing death. But their minds were left wide open because that was their only way to escape, since the war was too unbearable for them to accept.'
Vasko Stamboliev, First Place Winner

AGES 14–16

## Me Brother Dan

*by Molly Meleady-Hanley (Written in the Sheffield Dialect)*

Me brother Dan went off to war, marching
down Duke Street with his Pals.
Heads held high, while the Sheffield crowd
clapped and cheered them so!
Me Mam wept and me Dad said:-
"Gi'ore Molly. Be proud. Be happy for our lad.
He's serving his King and Country in a just war".

Six Weeks later, we got a fancy Can Can card
from our Dan
Reet chuffed we were. Dad read it out , puffed
up chest, loud and clear.
Dad said, Dan was doing well and our Dan
wished us all good cheer.

Tucking card in't pocket, he went off down road
to get hisen a beer.
Ten weeks later, on Skye Edge Fields, a
neighbour came calling us from play.
Saying :- " Come quick Lizzie, yer Mam needs
yer- reet away"
Opening our door, on Talbot Row, we heard
Banshee screaming
Our Mam, paper crumpled on't floor, sobbing
and rocking, hands to heaven.
"Why did he have to die? Me son, me son, me
only son!" she cried.
Dan's body never came home.

He lies without us, in some distant land.
In a place me Mam will never be able to go.
And so she trudges every day to Norfolk Row.
Saying prayers and lighting holy candles for our
Dan and other mother's sons.
These other boys whose lives too, will never
grow.

And me, well…I keep asking mesen
"Why do they kill caterpillars and then
complain that there are no butterflies?"
Me Dad said:- " Listen up our Lizzie. Them
there caterpillars and butterflies have died to
keep us all safe and free
You'll learn that one day me love, when you're
wise from being worn with care.
Until then me Liz, be proud and thankful for
the sacrifice our Dan and is Pals made for thee.

## AGES 14–16

### Deliverer and Receiver
*by Nancy Criddle from Burton-on-Trent*

Deliverer:
He's the one, who will deliver the news,
The fateful letter held tight in his hand,
Only he knows what she's about to lose,
He is so sorry, he understands.

The knocks on the door that summon the widow,
Are echoes of the fallen, the dead and the fighting.
She is not prepared, she does not know,
The sadness traced into this writing.

Receiver:
Is this the day she has waited for?
The day she'll lose what she loves most?
She's anticipated that knock on the door,
When she finds out he's now a ghost.

The man is sorry, he understands,
He hardly speaks but hands a letter,
Her husband does no longer stand.
Grief never heals, no it never gets better.

## AGES 14−16

## Win Some Lose Some
*by Vivian Huang from Cheltenham Ladies' College, Cheltenham*

## AGES 14–16

### I Miss You

*by Vasilisa Frolova from Art School of Olga Nazarkina, Deep River, Canada*

AGES 14–16

## The Poppy

*by Becki Pinkerton from the Royal School Armagh – Combined Cadet Force, Armagh*

Under the ground of the battlefield I grow,
I symbolise the memory of fallen heroes from long ago
I am an emblem for all to show
Their respect to so many whom they did not know.
I am a common field poppy – Papaver rhoeas
An elegant wildflower, distinctive and red
I'm the only one to grow in barren battlefields
I'm a comforting blanket, for our heroes alas dead.
In 1918 Monia Michael created me in silk
That I could be an emblem to last and not wilt
And in the UK on 11th November 1921
I became the flower on which Remembrance Day was built.
That was such a long time ago
Yet each year I am out there on show
Representing men, women and animals
Who gave their lives for the peace we now know.
So perhaps this year on Remembrance Sunday
You could give me a little place
On the Jacket, or jumper you're wearing
I won't take up very much space
Would you wear me with pride as you remember?
Yes I'm the red leaf, black centre and green stem
I represent the sacrifice of ordinary people
Caught up in wars not created by them.
I have no religious conviction
I just happened to grow where many fell
So will you help me to say 'We will remember them'
And their stories to our children tell.

**AGES 14–16**

### The Great War – The Great Theatre

*by Julian Ting from Garden International School, Kuala Lumpur, Malaysia*

Truth.
That is a…
Podium for you to celebrate. Just think of it.
There is no
Better way to serve your country.
There is a
Sense of gratification
Sense of reward
Sense of remembrance
As there is no
Fear.

The last moment of war just
Full of triumph and courage.
There is no moment
Of grief from your family.
The product of war is only
Your family's love, yet,
What must be cherished:
Peace after war and,
Who can deny it?

(Now read from bottom to top)

AGES 14–16

## Of Family, Of Nation, Of Home
*by Yan Xing Lee from Malaysia*

*'The calibre of the entries this year has been of an incredibly high standard once again. The depth of thought, interpretation of the subject, creativity and imagination in many of the entries has been outstanding and really impressive.'*
Michael Langmead, Art Judge

AGES 14–16

## Prisoner of War

*by Mina Soso from London*

AGES 14-16

## Realm of No Man's Land

*by Lucy Ozich from Cashmere High School, Christchurch, New Zealand*

Come, grace me with a muddied foot and a muddied face.
Push off and forwards with dampened breath and stagnant water thin.
Take a risk with rotten white and open needy palms.
And join me lying, deep in dust.  Enter no man's land.

Be at peace with what you've done, and what you may soon do.
Put your faith in one man's soul, raise that torn flag up and out.
It's a crime of war to gun you down, but who would ever know?
People change, for good or bad, here in no man's land.

It's in God's grace that you are here, you have a part to play.
Take in a breath, sharp and cold, piercing, ragged, thin.
Wait a moment, the choice is yours.  To stand or turn and run,
You can't help it, no one can, the thoughts of no man's land.

It may matter much, the choice you make, once your hand is raised
So allow yourself to fall away, and raise that hand up high.
You are a cost in an endless story, your moment has just passed.
Did you do what must be done, in the realm of no man's land?

## Misneachd na Pioba

*by Hamish Scott from the Isle of Harris*

Ceòl is seinn,
Danns is leum
Sonas is aoibhneas a' lìonadh an rùm
Agus ann am meadhan an spòrs,
Tha am pìobaire.

Fuaim cuilc is dosan
"Drill" is ullachadh
Sgìth an deidh trèanadh
Agus anns na "barracs"
Tha ceudan de phìobairean

Peilearean is sligean-cogaidh
Gunnachan is "gas"
Mì-chìnnt anns a' bhlàr-chatha
Agus ann am meadhan an aimhreit
Tha am pìobaire.

Sprùilleach is cuirp,
Sgàpte air feadh an àit,
An sàmhchair is an ciùineachd air caochladh
Le breislich cogaidh,
Agus ann am meadhan an sgrios
Tha phìob mhòr  treígte air an raon, gun ghleus.

Ceud bliadhna air adhart…

Crom-luis is blàth-fhleasgan
Sailm is bàrdachd
Agus anns a' mheadhan,
Ceòl le speís is onair
Aig  Piobaire.

## Inspiration of the Bagpipes

*by Hamish Scott from the Isle of Harris*

Music and song,
Peace and joy pervading the room,
In the centre of the hilarity
The Piper plays

Sounds of reeds and drones
Drill and preparation
Tired after exercises,
And in the barracks
Hundreds of Pipers

Bullets and shells
Guns and Gas
Uncertainty on the battlefield,
Central to the chaos
Is the Piper

Devastation abounds
Bodies scattered around
Peace and quiet shattered
By the turbulence of war,
In the middle of destruction
Forsaken on the ground
The 'Piob Mhor'* abandoned and tuneless

100 years later...

Poppies and Wreaths
Psalms and Poems
Central to it all
Music and respect with Honour
From the Piper.

* *great Highland Bagpipes*

### Rhyfel yn yr Awyr

*by Gwawr Griffiths from Ysgol Syr Thomas Jones, Amlwch*

O na! Rhedwch! Symydwch!
Clywaf swn iarwm
Fel humion yn fy nghlust
Pobl yn rhedeg
A plant yn crio

Gwelaf adar yn y man
Agosau ac agosau y fydden nhw
Swn ciecian fel tic toc y cloc
Edrychaf I fyny
Mae'r Zeppelin wedi cyrraedd!

Yn yr awyr bydd y fflachio
Fel storm uwch fy mhen
Pryd bydd tawelch
Cadwaf yn agos at mam
Rhoddais I mi sicrwydd

*Translation*

## War in the Sky

*by Gwawr Griffiths from Ysgol Syr Thomas Jones, Amlwch*

Oh no!  Run!  Move!
Hearing the alarm noise
Like a hum in my ear
People are running
Children are weeping

I see birds in the distance
Getting closer and closer
Now noise like the tick-tock
Of a clock
I look up
And the Zeppelin has arrived

In the sky there is flashing
Like a storm above my head
When will be the quiet?
I keep close to my mother
She gives me comfort.

## AGES 9–11

# WW1 Quilt

*by King Henry VIII and Cantref Primary, Abergavenny; Osbaston CW School, Monmouth; Usk CW School and Caldicot Secondary*

*130 pupils took part in 10 funded school-based, artist-led workshops, through the Young Arts Programme of Monmouthshire Decorative and Fine Arts Society (MDFAS) affiliated to The Arts Society, to commemorate the First World War.*

## AGES 9–11

### Sweetheart Brooches

*by Kaksha Chandarana, Elizabeth Da Teresa, Lydia Lam, Zelal Cam, Omar Said, George O'Mahoney, Adelina Cerniukaite Musa, Anastasia Elias, Taranom Hosseinpour, Leo Braviak, Sophie Kuzia, Zuzanna Kaczmarczyk Mrs Ann Richards and Mrs Elizabeth Brimson from Sunnyfields Primary School*

*'A hundred years have passed and the original generation affected by the First World War are all departed. But their experiences, their sufferings, their emotions and the lessons we learned are once more revived and spread throughout the world by our youngest generation as witnessed by their contribution in the Never Such Innocence Poetry and Art competition during these last three years on the hundredth anniversary of the First World War.'*
Androcles J. Scicluna, Poetry Judge

## AGES 9–11

### Somewhere Among the Clouds Above
*by Ruben White from County Donegal, Republic of Ireland*

## AGES 11–14

### War Terror
*by Ken Dunphy from Kilrossanty National School, County Waterford, Republic of Ireland*

In August 1914 the start of the war
Irish men in their thousands answered the call
To help free small nations the newspapers read
For these hungry men t'was the need to buy bread

Dublin city at the start of the war
Was a place of hunger, sadness and poor
The men had no jobs the lockout still strong
No money, no food, no doctor, all wrong

The answer to their sad plight then
to France went these bold brave men
Thousands died, thousands injured
Why, oh why, their children cried

*'As we strive to remember all of those who sacrificed their lives, health and security in that world-wide conflict, our children can teach us so much through the simplicity of their art, poetry and prose. Glasnevin Trust are proud to be associated with the Never Such Innocence Project, whereby our histories can be commemorated by our children.'*
George McCullough, CEO Glasnevin Trust

## War

*by Conor Birks, Amy Massey and Layla Shaw from Abbey Hulton Primary School,
Stoke-on-Trent*

It must be scary in the war,
I shudder at what you saw.
I wonder what the war was like,
As so many people went out to fight.
The war took over land, air and sea,
I give thanks that you fought for me.
So many men battled on through,
They knew what they had to do.
Sailors on ships had to think,
Of ways to make sure they did not sink.
Those sailors we called the Navy,
Who went out on oceans wavy.
Those who counted bullets with maths,
And the ones who followed and stuck to the paths.
So we go and mark the land,
Some of us may need a helping hand.
Let us give thanks, it can't hurt us,
Even if we're on a bus.
Soldiers sent letters to people like me,
Maybe one for you, could it be?

## Echoes Across the Century: A Memory Box

*by Frankie Barber from St Jude and St Paul's Church of England Primary School, London*

# हामीलाई बिर्सनु हुँदैन

## (Forget Us Not)

*by Joel Brassington from The de Ferrers Academy, Burton upon Trent*

We are the unsung heroes,
The ones who were forgot.
This was not our war to fight,
But fight it, did we not?
Have you let your discriminatory accidentals overcome our sacrifice?
Are we not worth the effort to celebrate?
We fought with you.
We suffered with you.
We died with you.
Why are we not worth as much?
Is one life more valuable than the other?
Why?
Why have you forgotten us?
Why have you forgotten our sacrifice, and yet – not your own.
Were they not the same?
History is written by the winners in life.
Did we not win?
But we ask future history,
And generations to come,
Forget us not.

Why did we come so far from our home, our friends, family?
Wives and children – safe at home.
Did we come: to be shunned, worthless, forgot?
No.

We came because we are a part of your whole, your body.
Is one part of the body less important than another?
Could you succeed without a toe, a lung, a finger?
Would life be agony without a toenail, left hand, an ear?
To join you we have given up these luxuries:
Legs, eyes, hands.
Do we deserve to be forgotten?
No.
We are the unsung heroes,
The ones who were forgotten;
Forget us not.

We toiled, we worked, we died,
Forget us not.

So when you tell your children, and they tell theirs,
Do not forget to tell them of our great sacrifice,
For we are the Gurkhas of the Great War, the unsung heroes, so
remember us.

## Lest We Forget (Sign Language - Must Not Forget)

*by Alice Dorey from Knowl Hill School, Pirbright*

### The Somme Cup
*by Freddie Hawkins from King's College School, London*

A crowd of 60,000 strong, heaving and ecstatic,
thronged along the Paris pitch at Easter.
Then sacrificed, like Christ himself.
New Zealand gave its players up to maul
and be mauled.
The congregation met on the distressed earth,
marked by scrums and shells.
Lift him up, your comrade, in the line out.
Set and lock, then rent apart.
'In the bonds of love we meet',
**O nag iwi matou ra**.

In Belgium, crowds, drowned out by shelling,
saw the players steeling at the ruck.
And freedom flew unfettered from the wreckage.
In the charge down, muscles were not wasted,
but iron and sinew, counter rucking madly.
Faces pressed to ground smelled home's green pitches,
not the fetid earth of clay and bootpress.
At the breakdown, limbs entwined,
the allies reached out to bind.
'God defend our free land',
**Me aroha noa**.

*Continued...*

Through Zeitoun's dunes the players ran, blindsided,
and strafed the low tide pitch at Lemnos.
No torsos mutilated by the volleys,
only rage transformed and lines defended.
There the acned scrum half heard his mother,
Don't get hurt now. Keep well back from others.
But there is no keeping back in trenches,
so she keeps a parlour light to guide him
home along the maimed path to her door.
'From the darts of strife and war',
**Kia tau to atawhai.**

Do you hear them calling now from stadiums silenced?
Boots unlaced, trophies unlifted.
From Paschendale and Messines, 'McNeece" and 'Baird'.
In Paris, 'Bobby Black' and 'Turtill' are heard.
As tides reclaim the names of 'Dewar', 'Downing',
Gallipoli, where they lay pale and bleeding,
New Zealand's losses were too great to bear.
How can we give our thanks unbounded,
to those whose passion for the game we share?
'Hear our voices we entreat',
**Ata whakaranwgona.**

Now, when we feel the pressure and the drive,
with lungs that burst and crowds that chant our names,
we too belong, stand strong as brothers.
But futures safe from gas and trigger.
And afterwards in bruised and raucous glory,
we chorus, celebrating in their honour.
The Moascar Cup held high with pride and sorrow.
For every light, in every home,
that welcomes our return,
'We will remember them',
**E kore ratou e koroheketia**.

*(Note: Quotations (translations) and bold text are taken from the 'Ode of Remembrance' and the 'New Zealand National Anthem' in the Order of Service for the 2015 Commemoration of The Battle of Messines, remembering those New Zealand rugby players killed during the First World War and their tour of Europe, called the 'The Somme Cup'.)*

## Time Never Obscures You

*by Danfeng Cai from Alliance Art Academy, Canada*

## Colourful World

*by Denley Casey, Bobby Smith, Ezekiel Critchlow, Kayla Turton, Tegan Davis, Dion Williams, Kameron Driver, Melissa Williams, Holly Gillham, Sorrel Williams, Tyler Goddard, Hayley Wood, Caitlin Goodsir-Jones, Anne Grady, Molly Hagan, Jamie Hirons, Angel Kendall-Chambers, Ruby Lewis, Tabetha Mansell, Scott McArthur, Grace Michael, Yaris Pritchard, and Kaydee Rowlands, from Ysgol y Tywyn, Holyhead*

No more dark days
Or being scared
No more fighting
Or being afraid

For being brave
And the love you gave
We'll remember you always

(CHORUS)
Because this is a
Colourful world
We love our
colourful world
This is a
Colourful world
Because of you

*Written in a workshop facilitated by Never Such Innocence Artist in Residence Bethzienna.*

**Nothing Good Comes of War**
*by Georgia Green from the British School of Paris, Paris, France*

Nothing Good Comes of War
Beaming in my smart new uniform, stomach full of butterflies,
I had just finished my training course and was ready to take to the skies,
Props turning, chocs away, runway gleaming in the moonlight,
Throttle back and, like a bird, I soared off into the night, It was all an exciting adventure back then, a child's game,
Until I saw the real destruction and I hung my head in shame,

And I thought to myself,
What was all of the fighting for,
Nothing good comes of war,

I flew over the sombre soldiers cramped into the winding trenches,
Lifeless and limp, hunger and pain etched on their grimy faces,
The endless blaring thunder of guns grasped their breaths away,
Every inch of bare skin masked in filth standing in the mud and hay,
They sighed at every extreme explosion that stole brave soldier's lives,
All the great things I was told of war was just a bunch of lies,

And I thought to myself,
What was all of the fighting for,
Nothing good comes of war,

I moved on gliding peacefully into the starry night,
Until I caught a glimpse of an equally frightful sight,
Buildings ruined, people homeless and hurt on the rubble-scattered street,
Forlorn and forgotten, bare and burnt stands a solit'ry tree,
Restless lost souls awake from their slumber howling in the wind of sin,
Grief and hopelessness hovers in the air above the din,

And I thought to myself,
What was all of the fighting for,
Nothing good comes of war,

I swooped above the terrible sights, high in the flawless sky,
Who could be this cruel to their own kind I feel a tear in my eye,
I had to join the war for my country, to help fight,
Now I see that I was out of my mind to think this was right,
But luckily the trying times will pass, as they always do,
This war will have to end soon so put on a smile and you will live through.

## War Brothers

*by David Potocnik Hahonina from London, Canada*

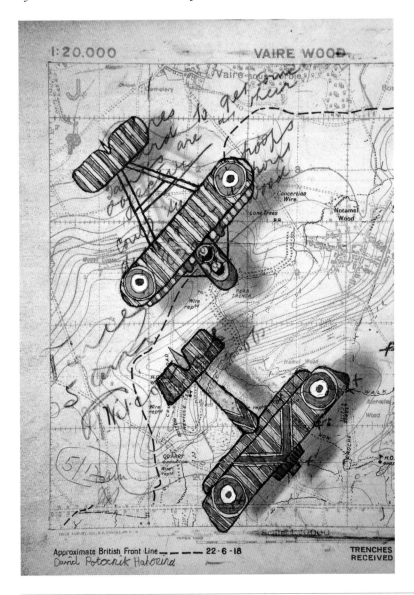

'The Royal Air Force is very proud to partner with NSI and we share an aim to inspire the young people of today, so that your voices are heard as we commemorate those who have gone before. Through your words, music and pictures, the events of 100 years ago will never be forgotten and they will inspire future generations in the same way that the artists of 100 years ago captured the essence of war in their poems, paintings and songs.'

Air Chief Marshal Sir Stephen Hillier, Chief of the Air Staff

### The Airman

*by Thomas Callander from St. Cedd's School, Chelmsford*

A rumble in the sodden streets
A glint of sunlight in the polished propeller
The waxed wing emerging from shadow
And up, up, up, off into the blazing sun

A streak of shadow in the sunlit sky
Sleek shapes define structure and speed,
Weaving between the velvet clouds

A wisp in the wind
A whisper in the trees
A wail in the woods
As down, down he flies

Blood encrusting against his dishevelled skin
Curdling around his worn leather booties
Vision blurring
Blackout…

 WAR IN THE SKIES

## Untitled
*by Kedaton Campbell from the United States of America*

## The Sopwith Camel

*by Freiya Elton from Malvern St James Girls' School, Malvern*

Innocence leads them to the door,
They eagerly anticipate it, striving for more.
Naivety drags them to the plane site,
They get into their sop and fly such a height.
Into a dogfight they go, malice everywhere,
Pilots twisting, turning and diving through the air.
The whirring and the purring,
The sparring the spurring.
The losing, the winning
The falling, the spinning.
Innocence lures them to another fight
Making them decide what's wrong and what's right.
Naivety leads them to their death,
The sop shuddering to an end, like their last breath.

*'Helping judge was both enjoyable and moving. As an ex-soldier myself, I am so pleased that the activities, efforts and sacrifices of my forebears remain strongly in the consciousness of our children.'*
Philip Harris, Poetry Judge

AGES 11–14

WAR IN THE SKIES

## The Wind Carries Us

*by Tessa Blandin from Île-de-France, France*

## Sky Battle

*by Freya Ling from The Folkestone School for Girls, Folkestone*

Hurry, hurry don't be hasty,
A world above is waiting for you,
The larks fly high as the plane dives.
Bullets dance in the air,
Striking the heart of pounding metal.

Soar in low,
Below the clouds,
Aim and fire without a doubt.
Smoke billows in the air engulfing all in range,
Streaks of metal and lead, heart beats faster
pounding ever more,

Pull up, pull up, the atmosphere is thin,
Dive, dive, hit 'em.
Be careful though,
You might not stick the landing.

Water, water, fills the cockpit,
Better go faster wedge it open,
Lungs screaming,
Heart racing ever faster,
Till it stops be known a martyr.

Diving, swerving for ever more,
Immortalised in feats of glory.
Still the larks fly,
As do I,
In my dreams of pride,
Joy and sacrifice.
The larks fly high in the sky.
Cockpit, mayday, home.

## In Flanders Field
*by Clara Mateos-Shepherd from Sheffield*

'I am delighted that so many children entered Never Such Innocence's War in the Skies Competition from across the Globe. The quality of their work is extraordinary and thought provoking, and demonstrates a level of insight that is a credit to them all.'
Air Vice-Marshal Mike Wigston, Assistant Chief of the Air Staff

## Guardian

*by Kutloogh Qureshi from The Tiffin Girls' School, Kingston upon Thames*

Blue. White. Red
Engine and heart roar as one
Wild metal.
I can taste valour in the air

It's easy to fly and forget,
Drunk on sunlight
like that six-year-old in a cardboard plane
sodden in the August rain

The sky is free like dreams:
She's beautiful and sinister
Unconquered.
Celestial and raw

And it hurts.
The bitter guns and
Black smoke burn
I see her tortured face

Blue. White. Red
I will defend,
In Person, Crown and Dignity
Courage calls.

And our hearts roar as one
For the barley fields
And the boys in cardboard planes
For freedom.

And I'm not afraid:
Let the wind whisper my story
Of summer days and the
Ones I loved

Capture my colours
In the constellations
They'll look and remember
What we gave

Through struggles to the stars.

AGES 14–16  WAR IN THE SKIES

## In memory of the war in the sky
*by Bianca Gegea from Romania*

## THE F(L)IGHT
*by Ayushi Bhat from Orpington*

When I was young,
I thought they were birds.
Soaring day and night,
Without any fatigue.
Close to each other,
Darting about fearlessly.
Gliding with pride…

Now I am older,
I know they were planes.
With bombs so cruel,
With pilots so valiant.
Risking their lives,
Losing their families.
To keep others safe…

Birds and Planes,
Freedom and Flight.
Duty and Sacrifice,
For Pleasure and Peace.
Beautiful memories cherished,
Haunting feelings entwined.
Forever to be remembered!

## Fragmented Flight

*by Catalina Taylor from The British School of Paris, Paris, France*

# INTRODUCTION

In 2016 Never Such Innocence Founder, Lucy French met Dave Stewart of the legendary band the Eurythmics and his business partner Jono Hart. Having mentioned Never Such Innocence and the extraordinary entries received from children in both poetry and art, Dave and Jono immediately said, "why don't you do song, a song is a poem put to music". After numerous transatlantic emails and calls, Songs of the Centenary was born.

This new strand to the project gives children the opportunity to use music to reflect on the events of 100 years ago. In order to support children and teachers we provided free in-school songwriting workshops, initially developed by Marty Longstaff of the band The Lake Poets who became our first Artist in Residence. We then took on another singer-songwriter, Bethzienna. Marty and Bethzienna have toured the UK and Europe to deliver workshops enabling children of all abilities to write and perform songs. Children worked in groups or individually and we have been impressed by the music and lyrics that children from all over the world have produced. We also created an online platform, powered by Trackd, providing a secure environment to create music. You will find a selection of the lyrics on the following pages.

Songs of the Centenary was supported by IVE, Mappin & Webb and the Lethersellers' Company Charitable Fund.

## Fighting on my Own

*by Lara Vujasevic from Piper's Corner School, High Wycombe*

Somebody said go and join the war
My mother had to show me the door
Holding a gun in my hand
Am I strong enough to kill a man
Now the enemy is coming and I have just got to defend myself

{Chorus} I am in the war now fighting for Britain
Too scared to fight now I don't want to be here
I am giving it my all, am scared that I won't come home
Fighting this war on my own

They brought in some new soldiers
There's one called Jack we have grown closer
Come on some bombs all around, Jacks fallen to the ground

{Chorus}
So far away, but still so near, fighting this war with fear
I don't know what to do but cry
I just watched my best friend die

{Chorus x2}
So far away but still so near, I know my future will be clear
War has come to an end.

## This Girl Can

*by Amber Jones, Callum Bainbridge, Ella Crossley, Elle Steel, Steven Clark, Jamie Stubbs, Jessica Campbell, Courtney Smith, Scarlett Bewick, Mollie Smith, Dylan Douglas, Tianna Clark, Lydia Thompson, Natalya King, Maddison Smith, Benjamin Kempthorne, Daniel Large, Jasmine Goldsmith, Mika Reay and Aidan Brunton from Hasting Hill Academy, Sunderland*

Don't tell us that we cannot
The W.R.A.F. are coming in hot
You sit upon your golden throne
But all the while the bombs are thrown
We can do whatever the boys can do!

Yeah we can do whatever the boys can do!
The W.R.A.F. is coming for you!
We're going to prove the papers wrong
We'll fight so brave and sing our song
The W.R.A.F. is coming for you!

The girls who are up in the sky
Fight just as hard as fly as high
Fighting fit and ready to go
We'll make sure everybody knows
That we can do whatever the boys can do!

Yeah we can do whatever the boys can do!
The W.R.A.F. is coming for you!
We're going to prove the papers wrong
We'll fight so brave and sing our song
The W.R.A.F. is coming for you!

*Written in a workshop facilitated by Never Such Innocence Artist in Residence Marty Longstaff.*

## The Sky's the Limit

*by Alexandra Connie Aylott, Meriel MacLeod Boyd, Connie Eleanor Duncan, Milly Levi Mackay, Iona McDowall, Grace Newlands, Kimberley Isabell Alison Orr, Craig Rae, Chloe Scott, Claire Taylor, Emma Whyte and Charlotte Wright from Lossiemouth High School, Lossiemouth*

I wonder what is up there
hiding in the sky
Do the birds all know the answer?
If they do then why don't I?

I want to be there with them
An eye up in the clouds
Others born before me
Felt the same. They make us proud

For a hundred years we've tried
To reach the limits of the sky
We fly so high
And for a hundred years we've soared
And we will forever more
We fly so high

They fly into the heavens
Knowing they might die
I think of all their loved ones
And then tears fill my eyes
 I hear the sound of thunder
I'm shocked unto the core
We hear the planes pass by us
Set to face what is in store

For a hundred years we've tried
To reach the limits of the sky
We fly so high
And for a hundred years we've soared
And we will forever more
We fly so high

For a hundred years we've tried
To reach the limits of the sky
We fly so high
And for a hundred years we've soared
And we will forever more
We fly so high
We fly so high
We fly so high

*Written in a workshop facilitated by Never Such Innocence Artist in Residence Marty Longstaff.*

## Remember

*by Lydia Grigg from Stafford*

VERSE 1:
One, two, three steps across the border.
They see familiar soils, familiar water. They're home they're safe and yet their minds still suffer.
Yes, bruises fade but memories can't recover.

It's easy to forget the life that's been lost if it hasn't affected us.
It's hard to look at and read the name in stone, knowing they didn't return home.
But today we remember you
And always, we remember you.

VERSE 2:
They were told that they'd be home before the leaves fall,
Then autumn passed, then weeks, then months, then years formed.
The countless days they were away they did not know.
If they would die, survive, return and be alone.

It's easy to forget the life that's been lost if it hasn't affected us.
It's hard to look at and read the name in stone, knowing they didn't return home.
But today we remember you
And always, we remember you.

We are free because of you
We all believe because of you
And I want to thank you, thank you
Now we can all be individual and be who we want to, because of you.
(We remember you, we remember you)

But today we remember you
And always, we remember you.

# Together: A UK–German Centenary Project

## TOGETHER: A UK-GERMAN CENTENARY PROJECT

For the final year of the centenary we embarked on a youth-centred UK-German creative arts project with kind support from the British Council in Germany, British Embassy in Berlin, *Volksbund Deutsche Kriegsgräberfürsorge*, and UK-German Connection.

We invited young people aged 9-16 from the UK and Germany to work in partnership, or independently, to produce poetry, art or songs inspired by our shared history. We encouraged entrants to draw on the events of the First World War and create messages of hope and unity for the future.

Winners were chosen by a select group of judges in the UK and Germany and invited to a special event kindly hosted

Ambassador Sir Sebastian Wood at the British Embassy in Berlin. At the event, the winners showcased their work to a distinguished audience and were awarded Certificates of Commendation. A selection of entries may be found on the following pages.

## TOGETHER - GEMEINSAM: EIN BRITISCH-DEUTSCHES PROJEKT ZUM 100-JÄHRIGEN WELTKRIEGS-GEDENKEN

Im letzten Jahr des 100-jährigen Gedenkens an den Ersten Weltkrieg haben wir einen britisch-deutschen Jugend-Wettbewerb in den kreativen Künsten ausgeschrieben, der unterstützt wurde von der britischen Kulturorganisation British Council, der Britischen Botschaft in Berlin, dem *Volksbund Deutsche Kriegsgräberfürsorge* und der UK-German Connection, einer Initiative zur Förderung des britisch-deutschen Jugendaustauschs. Dafür möchten wir uns herzlich bedanken.

Junge Menschen zwischen 9 und 16 Jahren aus Großbritannien und Deutschland waren dazu eingeladen, allein oder zusammen mit anderen Gedichte, Kunstwerke oder Songs zu kreieren, die von unserer gemeinsamen Geschichte inspiriert sind. Die Wettbewerbsteilnehmer*innen waren aufgefordert, mit Bezug auf die Geschehnisse des Ersten Weltkriegs

Botschaften der Hoffnung und Einigkeit für die Zukunft zu erschaffen.

Die Gewinner wurden von einer Gruppe ausgewählter Preisrichter*innen in Großbritannien und Deutschland bestimmt, und waren zu einer besonderen Veranstaltung in der Britischen Botschaft in Berlin eingeladen, die freundlicherweise von Botschafter Sir Sebastian Wood ausgerichtet wurde. Hier konnten die Gewinner ihre Arbeiten einem distinguierten Publikum präsentieren und erhielten ihre Ehrenurkunden überreicht. Eine Auswahl der Wettbewerbsbeiträge wird auf den folgenden Seiten vorgestellt.

## On the battlefield

*by Alexandra Sliwinska from Gesamtschule Berger Feld, Gelsenkirchen, Germany*

## A Poem for Peace

*by Sky O'Flynn from the United Kingdom*

Little poppy given to me,
Help me keep the world safe and free
I'll wear a poppy as red as can be,
To show that I remember those who fought for me

May all the people know peace and tranquillity,
May all the people live in their land peacefully,
Let us all work and play in serenity
As we stand together in perfect unity

### Let it be peace

*by Lena Reermann from Gesamschule Elsen, Paderborn, Germany*

The war was a very long
and hard time,
the soldiers were brave
each one was not worth dying.
this pathetic war,
soldiers fought to protect us.

We hope they live in peace
and quiet in heaven,
without pain and war,
many soldiers have died
and families have suffered.

It was not a real family anymore,
just a family with an invisible father,
but we will never forget our protectors,
they will stay in our memories.

Let's make art rather than war,
let us live in peace,
let's make the world colourful
and not black, grey and empty,
let's bring life into the world.

## Peace
*by George Sanders from Hampton School, Hampton, United Kingdom*

## All the same

*by Joyce Tam from Victoria College, Belfast, United Kingdom*

I am not a good soldier
I do not understand–
What divides us to point our guns, lies only
A fine line separating man from man

Hear the bullets raining down and piercing
The hopeful hearts of wives and children
Through the ragged burn of each inhale, simply close your eyes and envision
A New Year's Eve once again.

Crawl through this blanket of fear to me
Forget the anguish pooled in my eyes
As you watch the light fade from them,
Pray our children live to see the sun rise.

United, we fight for our own justice
My land, My country, My pride
I've pledged to protect my family
Only to take the same away from another man

For those of whom belong to mothers unborn
I bless you with a vision
Us who have brought up these indifferences
Will remain history once and for all.

## Lasting Legacies

*by Scott Anderson, Harvey Jones, Joshua Campbell, Jack Kennedy, Kathryn Williams, Emily Garner, Shannon Mermet, Chloe McGeoush, Caitie Edwards and Caitlyn Williams from St. Vincent's School for Sensory Impairment, Liverpool, United Kingdom*

## Friends of the Future

*by Alina Beier and Osman Sönmez from Gesamtschule Hattingen, Hattingen, Germany*

*Verse 1* – I have a map in my hand
My compass points the way
North the stranger
And south, my friend

*Verse 2* – I am proud of my troupe
But I want to be a child
I want to grow up
Before I die

*Chorus* – Why should I walk in the line?
When I could lose these friends of mine?
Why should I risk my dear life?!
Why should I care to clean my hands?
If I'm bound to soak in blood?
Why should we risk our lives?!

*Verse 3* – See the poppy hanging there
Its crimson head
It weeps for our dear young lives,
Linked by a thread

*Verse 4* – Will one day someone
Pluck it and think of me?
Will one day you and I
Be brothers and be free?

*{Chorus}*

*Verse 5* – Will there come a time to dine,
And Listen to the music?
And drink a glass of wine
All together?

*Verse 6* – Will there be more days to come?
On which we'll get to sing
Not only on Christmas,
But all the other days?

*{Chrous x2}*

Boy Scouts, learning how to be decent and proper and being taught that the boys on the other side are totally different. Coming to the realisation that this is not the case. We are all the same and coming to terms with the lies of the establishment. Wanting to fight for a better and unified future.

Das Lied handelt von Teilen der Boy Scouts / Pfadfinder, welche lernen sollten, anständige Menschen zu werden und denen beigebracht wurde, dass die Menschen der anderen Seite gänzlich anders als sie selbst seien. Weiterhin geht es um die Erkenntnis, dass gerade dies nicht der Fall ist. Wir sind alle gleich und die Kinder und Jugendlichen erkannten die Lügen der Führung und kämpften daher für eine bessere und gemeinsame Zukunft.

*Developed in a workshop facilitated by Never Such Innocence Artist in Residence Marty Longstaff.*

## Don't You Cry
*by Olivia Goede and friends from Germany*

*Chorus* – Little child don't you cry
There's a world behind this hell
Where your mother holds you tight
Little child don't cry
Don't cry

*Verse 1* – In the darkness they sit all close together
It is war, it is
It's in the air but no one dares to say
It's the thunder says a mother to her child
Don't be afraid
I won't leave you alone

*{Chorus}*

*Verse 2* – The darkness covers the light of the candle
Every siren tears up the tense silence
People's hearts scream for peace and freedom
And the children burn in the fire of fear
But don't be afraid
You won't be alone

*{Chorus}*

*Verse 3* – People are trying to stay strong
They try to keep a light
For a light, no matter how small
Can charge hope
They dance together in the rain
Cause together we are strong
Stronger then the darkness of war
With hope we can live on

## Weine nicht kleines Kind

*durche Olivia Goede und Freunde von Deutschland*

*Chor* – Weine nicht kleines Kind
Es gibt eine Welt hinter dieser Hölle
Wo Deine Mutter Dich sicher in ihrem
Arm hält
Weine nicht kleines Kind
Weine nicht

*Strophe 1* – In der Dunkelheit sitzen sie
alle dicht beieinander
Es ist Krieg- es ist
Es liegt in der Luft, aber niemand wagt
es auszusprechen
Es ist der Donner, sagt eine Mutter zu
ihrem Kind
Hab` keine Angst
Ich werde Dich nicht alleine lassen

*{Chor}*

*Strophe 2* – Die Dunkelheit verhüllt das
Licht der Kerze
Jede Sirene zerreisst die angespannte
Stille
Die Herzen der Menschen schreien nach
Frieden und Freiheit
Und die Kinder verbrennen in dem
Feuer der Angst
Aber sei ohne Angst
Du wirst nicht alleine sein

*{Chor}*

*Strophe 3* – Die Menschen versuchen
stark zu bleiben
Sie versuchen ein Licht zu bewahren
Denn ein Licht, egal wie klein es auch
sein mag,
bewahrt die Hoffnung
Sie tanzen zusammen im Regen
Denn zusammen sind wir stark
Stärker als die Dunkelheit des Krieges
Durch die Hoffnung können wir
weiterleben

## In Blood Nothing Grows

*by Felix, Florian, Julia, Konstantin, Marie, Ida, Carolina, Celine, Hannah, Isabel, Karla, Alina, Ellinor, Lilly, Julius, Emmelie, Carlo, Svenja, Evelyn, Johann, Lynn, Tim, Hermann, Antonia, Stefania and Henning from F.F. Runge Gymnasium, Oranienburg, Germany*

*together with*

*Khush, Zaheb, Marisa, Khushi, Aashish, Fatemah, Alayna, Kiya, Thomas, Riya, Anaya, Zoha, Kaden, Selina, Nina, Rachel, Amr, Kashif, Remi, Ada, Ella, Janany, Ayn, Sergio, Vinisha, Esha, Jasmine, Eliza and Andrei from Claremont High School Academy, Harrow, United Kingdom*

Touted a hero, yet forced from his home
Stuck between worlds, with no place to roam
Hopeless and scared, unaware and unsure
Asking "Why are we here, what are we fighting for?"
Nameless superiors, controlling their fate
An Eagle, a Lion. A blindfolded race

Cornflower, Daffodil, Edelweiss, Rose,
Clover, or Thistle, in blood nothing grows

Violence then silence, the 'bad' and the 'good'
Hopes, dreams, and memories, left staining the mud
Trenches and fences, barbed wire and blasts
Senseless defences, and scars that will last
No one is pure, all carry their guilt
Let's tear down the borders that mankind has built

Cornflower, Daffodil, Edelweiss, Rose,
Clover, or Thistle, in blood nothing grows

Krieg bringt nicht Sieg sondern zerstört nur Leben
Danach sollte kein Mensch mit Herz streben
With Einigkeit, Recht und Freiheit should our lands
Strive for brotherly love and a joining of hands
Let us keep the peace, to keep us all safe
Stand up for each other, let's dare to be brave

Cornflower, Daffodil, Edelweiss, Rose,
Clover, or Thistle, in blood nothing grows
Cornflower, Daffodil, Edelweiss, Rose,
Clover, or Thistle, in blood nothing grows

*Written in a workshop facilitated by Never Such Innocence Artist in Residence Marty Longstaff.*

# ACKNOWLEDGEMENTS

**Never Such Innocence would like to thank all of the schools, educational settings and students that have engaged with the project between 2014 and 2018, and the following people and organisations for your unwavering support:**

Barry Alexander; Matt Andersen; Army Football Association; Australian High Commission; Charlie Barton; Meg Bateman; Major General Ben Bathurst; Greta Bellamacina; Group Captain Tim Below; Tim Betjeman; Peter Biggs; de la Billiere Trust; Birmingham Council House; Dr Jonathan Black; Councillor Philip Braat; The Rt Hon Karen Bradley MP; British Army; British Council; Alastair Bruce of Crionaich; Danny Buckley and family; Michael Burleigh; Charles Byrne; Canadian High Commission; Jessica Carlisle; HMS Caroline; Eleanor Carter; HE Janice Charette, Canadian High Commissioner to the United Kingdom; Commander Nick Chatwin; CH2M; Sergeant Scottie Clark; Combat Veteran Players; Commonwealth War Graves Commission; Coutts; Cubitt Consulting; Sam Cumming; Department for Digital, Culture, Media & Sport; Colin Diamond; Katherine Diamond; The Rt Hon Sir Jeffrey Donaldson; Rebecca Done; Ned Douglas; Emma Dowley; Ruaidhri Dowling; The Reverend Stephen Dunwoody; Eaton Park Estate; Edinburgh Castle; Education Scotland; Verena Effgen; Elizabeth College; English Heritage; Chris Evans MP; University of Exeter; The Lord Faulkner of Worcester; Jim Fellows; Luc Ferrier; The Rt Hon Mark Field MP; First World War Centenary Battlefield Tours Programme; Forgotten Heroes; Amanda Gerry; Glasnevin Trust; Glasgow City Chambers; Golden Bottle Trust; Andrew Gordon; Flash Gordon; Rick Graham; Clare Grindey; The Guildhall; Imam Asim Hafiz; The Rt Hon Matt Hancock MP; Lieutenant Colonel David Hannah; Philip Harris; Jono Hart; Dr Anthony Harvey; Hattingen Comprehensive School; Glenn Hearnden; Air Chief Marshal Sir Stephen Hillier; Charles Hoare Nairne; Commander Steffen Handrick; Jessica Hodson-Walker; Professor Sir Deian Hopkin; The Rt Hon Earl Howe; Hyde Park Residents' Association; Martin Impey; HMS Iron Duke; Mark Jackson; JCG Foundation; Baroness Jenkin of Kennington; Melissa John; Stanley Johnson; Jones Day; Eirlys Jones; Gabriella Kardos; Patricia Keppie; Michael Langmead; The Leathersellers' Company; RAF Leeming; Rob Lewis; Rosi Lister; Baron Llewellyn of Steep; Marty Longstaff; RAF Lossiemouth; Zerrin Lovett; Museum for Macedonian Struggle; Aonghas MacNeacail; Sir John Madejski; Flight Sergeant Gill Malam; Sir Christopher Mallaby; The Manx Museum; Mappin & Webb; Marylebone Boys' School; Siobhan Matos; The Rt Hon Theresa May MP; Tula McFadden; Chrysoula Melidou; Michaela Morgan; Mosaic; Cheryl Moscowitz; Dr Daniel Mulhall; Dr Andrew Murrison MP; Newgate Communications; Dr Viv Newman; Alma Ní Choigligh; Nicholson Institute; The Rt Hon the Viscount Norwich CVO; Harry Oates; RAF Odiham; Brigadier-General Matthew Overton; William Packer; Helen Paterson; Air Vice-Marshal Ross Paterson; Caroline de Peyrecave; Elly Preston; Tony Pringle; Colonel Hugh Purcell; Holly Quin Ankrah; RAF Museum, Cosford; RAF Museum, London; RAF100; Iain Richards; Major General Mike Riddell-Webster; Hillary Robinson; Squadron Leader Jo Roe; Royal Air Force; The Royal British Legion; Royal Liverpool Philharmonic Hall; Royal Navy; Baron Maurice Saatchi; St Andrew's University; Matteo Schürenberg; Androcles Scicluna; Rupert Sebag-Montefiore; Russell Sheffield; Captain Chris Smith; Brigadier Bill Sowry; Jack Sowry; John Spurling; Stars Foundation; Dave Stewart; Sunderland Minster; Sunderland Music Hub; Thessaloniki City Hall; 13Hundred Creative Partners; Grant Tilbury; Andrew Todd; TreePress; Anna Trethewey; Guy Trouveroy; Nathalie Trouveroy; The Ulster Museum; RAF Valley; Velvet Coalmine Festival; Elaine Vosko; Professor Vlasis Vlasidis; Andrew Wallace; Victoria Wallace; Dr Anthony Wallersteiner; Robert Walters; David Ward; Warminster Garrison; The 6th Duke of Westminster; Westminster Foundation; Air Vice-Marshal Mike Wigston; Wild Search; Caroline Wilkes; Bethzienna Williams; Air Commodore Dai Williams; Brigadier Evan Williams; Steffan Williams; The Rt Hon Gavin Williamson MP; Liz Woodfield; WW100; WW100 Scotland; Jo Young

First published in 2018 by
Never Such Innocence
www.neversuchinnocence.com
Never Such Innocence. Registered Charity Number 1156148

Text and design © Never Such Innocence 2018
Poems, songs and artworks © the artists 2018

ISBN 978-1-9995872-1-5

Printed in China